Journey to Motherhood

Alison Freeland

JOURNEY to MOTHERHOOD

One Woman's Story of Triumph Over Miscarriage

PRENTICE
HALL
PRESS

New York London Toronto Sydney Tokyo Singapore

Prentice Hall Press
15 Columbus Circle
New York, NY 10023

Copyright © 1990 by Alison Freeland

PRENTICE HALL PRESS and colophons are registered trademarks
of Simon & Schuster, Inc.

Library of Congress Cataloging-in-Publication Data

Freeland, Alison.
    Journey to motherhood / Alison Freeland. — 1st Prentice Hall Press ed.
      p. cm.
    ISBN 0-13-692831-5 :
    1. Freeland, Alison—Health. 2. Miscarriage—Patients—United States—
Biography. I. Title.
RG648.F73 1990
362.1'98392—dc20   89-70049
                                                           CIP

Manufactured in the United States of America

10 9 8 7 6 5 4 3 2 1

First Edition

Hope deferred maketh the heart sick:
but when the desire cometh, it is a tree of life.

Proverbs 13:12

When I was still heartsick from my pregnancy losses, I reached for a book by someone who shared the depth of my disappointment, yet ultimately experienced the joy of having a child. I couldn't find that book.

The birth of my daughter, Jessica Grace, brought me the most profound joy, but I know there are many still fighting the disappointment of an ended pregnancy, and still waiting.

This book is for you, to help you believe.

Acknowledgments

Many thanks to Jonathan Dolger and Gail Winston for their help with this book, and my deepest gratitude to everyone who helped me physically, emotionally, and spiritually in my quest to have a baby.

Contents

Introduction

I knew my pregnancy was over when the radiologists spoke in low voices. They don't turn their heads and whisper when everything looks all right. As they viewed the image of my uterus on the sonogram screen, I heard the words "spontaneous cardiovascular activity?" in a questioning tone. That's a bad sign.

I spoke to the one nearest me: "It's over isn't it?" I said clearly.

She seemed surprised I could talk. "I'm just the technician," she finally answered, "I show the results to your doctor and he interprets them for you."

"But the results aren't good," I insisted.

"I just conduct the tests."

"The fetus is dead, right?" I wanted a straight answer.

"Look, I cannot talk to you. The doctor will."

Slowly I got dressed and walked across the hall to my doctor's office. Pregnancy had made me nauseous for almost three months, but now something new twisted my stomach. I could feel a knot forming—a disappointment knot, a bad-news knot, a life-just-turned-sour knot—and I swallowed hard to make my stomach relax.

"It's not good news," Dr. Balick said. The radiologist had already reached him.

"I know."

"Of course, there's a tiny chance the test was wrong . . ."

"But basically," I finished his sentence, "this pregnancy is over."

He didn't argue, but explained briefly about a missed abortion. The fetus had died, but my body thought I was still pregnant. If left alone I could eventually miscarry, but it would be better to have a D & C (dilation and curettage procedure) to clean out my uterus as soon as possible.

We looked at each other across his desk, as we had done so many times in the past four years. The sadness in his eyes mirrored my own, and again I thanked God for this doctor who wasn't afraid to relate to his patients.

"I'm okay," I said. "I think."

"I know."

We were quiet a moment and then he spoke, almost to himself, "This isn't like your other pregnancy losses. I'm not saying it isn't hard, but everything isn't on the line for you this time. You won't have to go through hell before it gets better. In a funny way, I can almost say I'm at peace about this. I think you know how to handle it."

I could feel my face stretch into a funny smile, one that had tears right behind it.

"Both you and Hugh know what to do, and you've got each other, and you've been through much, much worse."

I managed a low grunt, thinking of all the time we had both invested in my ongoing quest to have a healthy baby. The new receptionist even gasped when she saw the size of my medical file. "You've spent a lifetime in this office," she had said. "At least," I replied.

Dr. Balick was speaking again, "Look, after what you've been through, this situation is not so terrible. I mean, the good news is, you know you can get pregnant."

He was right, and I didn't expect him to say any more. I asked enough about a D & C to know I'd live through it, then stood up to leave. Right then I needed to collect my twenty-month-old daughter from the receptionist and get out of there. Most of all I needed to collect my thoughts before they exploded out of control.

"I'm not going to let my mind go this time, God," I said quietly as I put on my coat. "Half an hour ago I was pregnant and happy. Now it's over and my heart is sinking pretty fast. Help me get a handle on this, please."

Walking up 9th Avenue, I saw only the grayness of November in New York City. No snow was in the air, only a harsh chill that made people exclaim out loud when the wind slapped their faces. Holiday-time in Manhattan. In front of Lincoln Center tourists by the bus-load lined up at the curb, faces pressed to the windows to see the cultural center strung with tiny white lights.

My daughter, imprisoned in her giant snowsuit, sat quietly in the stroller as I walked faster and faster to keep from crying. Suddenly tears escaped down my cheeks and I skewed my face but couldn't stop them. With head bent I sank onto some stone steps, pulling the stroller in front of me like a shield.

Here we go again, I thought, as the tears came faster and I gulped for breath. All those expectations and dreams I've built are for nothing. They're over. There will be no summer maternity clothes, no baby arriving in July, and no little newborn to turn the house upside down again. What's worse, I'm walking around with this dead dream still inside me. Not only that, I'm still nauseated from pregnancy, and it's all for nothing. It's over, finished, the end, and I hate going through this; I just hate it.

Finally there were no more tears left to roll. Burying my face in my daughter's snowsuit, I mumbled aloud, explaining to her that I was okay, just terribly disappointed and mad and sickened that this was happening to me again. I could feel her breathing and knew she was looking down at me with her curious expression, wondering why I was sitting on the steps of Lincoln Center crying in front of all those people. For once she sat patiently while I composed my thoughts and my face, and got us moving again.

Going north on Broadway, I struggled to get a perspective on the situation. The tears had come so quickly this time. In the past it had taken a lot longer for the shock to wear off and the tears to fall. Maybe I was accepting this one faster. All the better. Maybe my heart would heal faster as well.

Slowly I let my thoughts turn to my first failed pregnancy four years before. It could never again be as bad as the first time. I saw myself sitting in bed, stunned by the situation, immobilized by shock, ignorance, and the effects of grief. I remembered my intense desire to get pregnant again right away, that week, in order to replace what I had lost. And I remembered how alone I had felt, suddenly separated from the millions of women who seemingly gave birth without a problem.

Out of necessity I had collected ammunition to help me fight off the despair and disappointment of an ended pregnancy. Then it happened again, and I had to fight even harder. When at last the baby came who finally made it, I put away the bad memories. I wanted never again to face an ended pregnancy with its fury, sadness, and discouragement. Now those familiar foes were appearing on the horizon for a third time, with a black cloud of depression close at their heels.

I had thought pregnancy loss was a closed chapter in my life and, consequently, tried hard to forget the experience. I hated being forced to bring the subject back into focus, but knew there were things I had learned before that could help me now. Gingerly I sifted through the memories. Filed in my brain were the events of four years—pregnancies, untimely losses, repeated disappointments, fears of trying again, the sweetness of final victory—and what I had learned in the process.

As I walked up the street, I found I could easily recall the physical effects and tiniest details of life following each of my losses. There were so many days and weeks when every medical diagnosis, every indication from my body, every pregnant woman on the street, and every phone call had brought the temptation to get depressed, and when anxiety hung so heavily around me all I wanted to do was sleep. But eventually I identified when I was getting set up for a fall, and learned how to avoid it.

It was right after my first loss that I realized I had a fight on my hands. It took a long time for me to understand that childbirth was something I would have to work for instead of take for granted. Once I knew I was in a fight I saw my choice: to be bitter and defeated or thankful and believing. That's when I learned about keeping the flag flying.

Looking back on both losses, I saw the initial days of adrenaline and raw pain, and then the quiet times when Hugh and I could assess the situation with calm hearts.

Throughout those years there were so many new strains on our marriage, yet I learned how much Hugh meant to me and how easy it is to let that slip. There was the day I bluntly asked him how he felt about the losses, and heard answers I didn't expect.

I could remember my most difficult time when I couldn't pull myself free from despair, and what had brought me to that point. And as the months dragged on, still with no baby, I had to resist the continued temptation to be bitter.

In retrospect, I could see that the turning point for me was in what I later called the lesson of the skylight, and in the relief I found in building up my mind spiritually so that I could find peace from the negative evidence stacked against me.

Also filed in my memory were remarks people made that encouraged me and comments that dragged me down. And there were the stories I collected of other women's victories that reminded me miracles could happen.

As I thought about those years, I realized I had dealt well with the losses and had moved on. I could do it again, only I would try to do it faster this time. I continued walking up Broadway, pulling my mental armor into position. By the time I reached our apartment I knew I could talk without crying. First I phoned my husband at work. "It's not good news, Hugh. This pregnancy is over; it's only a matter of time before I miscarry."

"Okay," he said slowly, "do you want me to come home?"

"No, I'm fine, really. I'm handling it okay."

"You know what to do, don't you?"

"Yes, and besides"—we finished the sentence in unison—"we have a daughter."

It was impossible to measure my thankfulness for the bundle of energy now climbing out of her snowsuit. On the other hand, knowing the joy of having a child made a miscarriage all the more difficult because I better understood what I was losing.

"Do you want me to make some phone calls?" Hugh asked.

"No, I can do it." It meant phoning our families and, like so many times before, hearing the hurt in their voices and their desire to be with us.

As I made the calls, I felt my heart grow calm. It was so much easier when I knew what to expect and could prepare for it. Even the knot in my stomach was relaxing, and I began to realize the possibility of handling this loss without the turbulence I had experienced previously. Maybe Dr. B was right; I did know what to do.

Even when I saw Louise my heart stayed peaceful. I visited her after the D & C, when both my body and mind finally accepted that I was no longer pregnant. A good friend, and newly pregnant, Louise greeted me with a quiet hug. It was scarcely a week since we had talked eagerly about having children and how glad we were to be pregnant at the same time.

At first we shuffled around each other awkwardly. I wanted to assure her I was okay, and she didn't know if talking about her pregnancy would make me feel bad. We finally settled in the kitchen, holding our coffee cups and fussing over a plate of croissants. At last she looked me in the eye and said, "You're really okay, aren't you?"

"Yes," I replied. "I'm not going to fall apart over this one."

"You're one tough lady."

I was surprised, not ever thinking of myself in those terms. I looked back at her, still calm in my heart even when I knew she was going on to have a baby without me.

"I think," I said slowly, understanding more even as I spoke, "that I'm so familiar with the emotional battle following an ended pregnancy, I can prepare myself before it hits. I'm not going to give in this time. I hate the loss. It makes my heart sick, but I'm not going to let it ruin my life."

Journey to Motherhood

1 . Having It All

It seems so long ago that I believed pregnancy to be effortless. I was not aware I believed it to be that way; I simply didn't include pregnancy in my list of what would require effort, sacrifice, and discipline in life.

In my early twenties I pieced together an image of my future that could only have come from magazines and too many novels. It included the ambitious combination of a perfect marriage, a big city, travel, glamour, service to mankind, and a fulfilling career. Children figured in the background because, as far as I knew, having children happened while you concentrated on more pressing matters.

I approached my thirties by getting married and moving to New York City in the same week. At the end of a year, my thoughts touched down briefly on pregnancy, and then took off again on the idea of becoming established in a job with even some of the glamour I expected out of Manhattan.

"Take me, take me," I said silently to the eight male partners of a design firm who needed someone to do their public relations. At 7 A.M., they lunged for bagels and jelly donuts from a basket in the middle of the table while I listed my credentials. I didn't know much about architecture, but I could recognize the appeal of a high-ceilinged, newly renovated, 200-man office overlooking Park Avenue.

That night my husband, Hugh, stared at his spicy Thai dinner. "My wife, the corporate woman," he said, poking at the chicken. "Now you'll carry a briefcase and leave memos on the mirror."

"I don't have the job yet," I reminded him.

"Oh, you'll get the job," he said. "The question is, why would you want it?"

"I can learn about architecture."

"Don't tell them that. They think you already know."

"Design," I insisted, "is a very important part of New York City."

"I don't think you're applying for a job, you're applying for an image." He waved his chopsticks over the table. "Conference tables, business lunches, meetings, and corporate clothing."

"Leave me alone," I said, suddenly irritated. Something in the Nuea Yang disagreed with my stomach, and I didn't feel like talking anymore.

The next day the architects called and offered me the job. Happily I said good-bye to the insecurity of free-lancing, long lines in the post office, and typing on the living room coffee table. I was headed for the land of fifteen-foot ceilings, support staff, and my own office with a computer terminal. Maybe it was time to go shopping for a briefcase.

At the front door I realized that in my mind, underneath the sound of applause, a small alarm was ringing. I sat down on the couch and listened.

"I think you're pregnant," said the alarm.

Can't be, I argued. I just got a new job.

"You feel sick."

It was the Thai food.

"It's been longer than that." Instead of shopping for a briefcase, I went to the drugstore and bought a home-pregnancy test.

I knew that, to placate the vague obligation I felt to have a baby one day, I had lessened my vigilance about birth control for two months. However, when the opportunity for the new job arose, I pushed the idea of having a baby back another year at least, and renewed my effort to prevent pregnancy. Had my timing gone awry? I would have to wait until morning to find out.

Hugh and I spent the next morning trying to ignore the chemical process taking place on the table in the corner of our living room. If the little dot didn't change color, I would have another cup of coffee and enjoy my day. If the dot turned blue, my life was going to be complicated. Hugh went off to work and, at 9 A.M., I marched over to the table and confronted an unmistakably blue dot.

"This is wonderful," Hugh said over the phone with genuine excitement. "My wife, a pregnant corporate woman. When will you tell the architects?"

Hours passed before I could pick up the phone and call the new job. Much of the time I stared out the window at our dismal view of a parking garage. Had I known I was pregnant even three weeks earlier I would have accepted the pregnancy in favor of a new job. But now that I had the job, the pregnancy seemed inappropriate. Worse yet, the pregnancy might cost me the job.

The personnel man said he would have to call me back. I pictured the architects looking up from their drawing boards and clucking. Who would want to start a public relations effort with a guaranteed interruption after eight months?

"Why don't you take the job, anyway," he said when he called back. "We'll see where things stand in eight months, and decide what to do then. Okay?"

I agreed and returned to my seat by the window. Now I had both: a new job and a pregnancy. The firm was willing to take a risk with me; I would give them my best effort. The situation was simple. Clearly I couldn't give my best efforts to both things, so the pregnancy would have to take second place.

My reasoning was logical for a healthy thirty-year-old who had never encountered one of life's major setbacks, and for one who knew nothing about pregnancy. I pictured myself working hard while quietly growing bigger for nine months until delivering a perfectly healthy baby. Then I would return to work, having found someone else to watch the child.

During the next few months, I still innocently believed pregnancy would require little effort on my part. I hadn't yet discovered the multitudes of women for whom conception, carrying to term, or delivering without risk requires every ounce of effort they can muster. Several of my friends had suffered miscarriages, but those were distant events to me. I could not personally relate to their experiences and never expected to be among their number.

Even the books I collected on my "pregnancy shelf" talked only of the stages of pregnancy, nutrition, and preparing for childbirth. They always seemed to include an illustration of a pregnant woman silhouetted in a window, caressed by sunlight, and a second frame of the same woman relaxing in a rocking chair, hand resting lightly on her curving stomach. They were happy books, showing what happens to normal women who have normal pregnancies. As far as I knew, they were written for me.

I did not yet understand that I should be thankful I even conceived. Pregnancy was still something I took completely for granted, and therefore didn't value very much. Depending on the day, my attitude about having a baby swung back and forth from enthusiasm to nonchalance and even doubt.

Mostly, I thought pregnancy was an adventure both challenging and deeply personal, and one that connected me to women of all time. On the other hand, I remained objective. Unlike some women who shop for maternity clothes the day they know they're pregnant, look forward to morning sickness, and agonize over color schemes for a nursery, I expected a baby to show up one day without a lot of help from me.

On some days I wasn't sure I wanted a baby at all. I hadn't been around many children and didn't know if I actually liked them. What if I didn't like my own? What made me think I wanted to be a mother? Watching women struggle onto city buses with an infant pinned under one arm and a folded stroller banging around their ankles fueled my doubts.

My new job made the prospect of childbearing all the more strange. Pregnancy did not fit in well with the pressured, business atmosphere. Out of 200 employees, only two other women had been pregnant while at the company. Both had returned to work six weeks after delivering the baby. During my days of client meetings, press conferences, and business lunches, pregnancy seemed more and more foreign to that environment. What had I done?

Among my coworkers I found myself down-playing my growing body as if to prove pregnancy would not slow me down. As my waistline grew, I wore extremely serious clothing in progressively larger sizes, never coming near the frilly tent dresses and maternity blouses commonly associated with pregnant women. When meeting clients I sat down fast, pushing my stomach under the conference table, and I was careful not to display my profile for any length of time. When the elevator broke one morning, I climbed fifteen flights of stairs to the office.

I could afford this attitude because I still believed being pregnant was easy, and was something I could do whenever I chose. Later on, when that belief lay in pieces around me, and the prospect of never having a baby stood like a wall in front of my face, my ambivalence vanished. Later on, when I pounded my fists into the couch, demanding my body to carry a healthy baby, I looked back in amazement at my former presumptions.

Had I known I had all the makings of a "high-risk" patient, I would have used some caution, but my strong body and history of good health lulled me into thinking anything I attempted physically would work. I grew up playing tennis, riding horses, skiing, and running around in general. I was not an athlete, but hadn't I done all right that time I went rock climbing, and that morning I ran ten miles? And what about when I got talked into driving a jeep down that ravine in Colorado?

In addition, I considered myself a spiritually-minded woman and appreciated the inner strength that resulted from it. My family really read the family Bible and held a quiet reverence for God, which ran underneath all the surface activity of our household. I had argued with and tested their beliefs, eventually embracing a set of spiritual laws that I believed governed life. My recent romance with the city lights had caused my spiritual interests to dim somewhat, but I was sure I was covered for a pregnancy.

Things worked out well for me, so why shouldn't having a baby be the same? In many instances it seemed my energy made up for lack of planning, and when I ignored the risks, they didn't catch up with me. I knew it was possible to face both tremendous demands in life and tremendous disappointments, but I didn't expect them to come from my own body, or from a process which, under normal circumstances, takes care of itself.

One warning flag that waved clearly in my family history might have told me trouble was coming. But I didn't think it applied to me. The story of my mother's difficulty with childbirth was part of my childhood. She had lost several pregnancies in the fifth and sixth months, had surgery to correct a problem in her uterus, and had gone on to have my brother and me.

The only part of her problem that we knew might affect me was the drug she took while pregnant. In 1954, her doctor prescribed diethylstilbestrol (DES), a synthetic estrogen, to take during her pregnancy. A popular drug, especially in the fifties and sixties, it was administered to between 3 and 6 million women in the United States for many reasons, including the prevention of miscarriages.

In the early 1970s, articles began to appear describing an unusual clustering of cases of young women with a rare form of cervical cancer. The common denominator was that their mothers had all taken DES while pregnant. In addition, it was revealed that there was no evidence DES actually prevented miscarriage; therefore, it was no longer prescribed for that purpose.

When I turned seventeen my mother told me about the recent findings, and the possible risks to my anatomy. No problem, I thought, with all the optimism of a high school senior. I agreed to see a doctor and have a Pap smear. While sitting in the waiting room I recognized for the first time the fear that can hang around a doctor's office. Your body, instead of belonging to you, becomes a thing for them to test and evaluate. It's made worse when they tell you all the ways your body can get sick that you never knew before.

I didn't like it at all, nor did I like the prospect of having a checkup every six months as they were suggesting. I felt fear closing its arms around me, and quickly made a silent agreement with God.

"I'll take care of my body," I prayed, eyes closed to shut out the waiting room. "I won't take drugs, won't use birth control pills, won't do anything that might mess up that area of my body, and I believe you'll take care of the rest and protect me from the cancers they talk about." I shook off the fear and left the office.

In the twelve years following that visit, I faithfully went for Pap smears, with no suspicious results. None of the doctors I saw found anything in my anatomy to alarm them or cause me to think I might have trouble bearing children. From what I knew of DES, it had not affected me.

When I became pregnant, I explained all this at the midwifery center on Manhattan's Upper West Side. On a friend's recommendation I went to check out their program, in which several certified nurse-midwives rotate in caring for a woman during pregnancy and delivery. I liked their belief of not allowing medical intervention unless absolutely necessary. After all, the unnecessary intervention of DES had caused enough problems in my life.

The coordinator of this group of midwives was Barbara Brennan, an imposing woman who had been delivering babies for twenty-five years. Since 1964, she had practiced at Roosevelt Hospital in Manhattan, the first private hospital to employ the services of midwives. Now in their own office, this group of midwives was still using the facilities at Roosevelt Hospital for labor and delivery, and had a physician on call twenty-four hours a day in case of emergencies.

The midwives' office was clean, peaceful, and low-key. I appreciated their willingness to take time with me, and their emphasis on the word *natural* in describing the childbirth process. It fit in with my image of the effortless pregnancy. As long as mine was a normal pregnancy, and of course mine would be, I could stay with the midwives and never see the associated physicians. I preferred things that way, and decided to deliver with them.

Under their care, I slowly gained respect for the life forming inside me. When I wasn't at work, I became more and more fascinated with my growing body. During one appointment I heard the baby's heartbeat and found my eyes filled with tears. There really was something inside me, and it was alive, and its heart sounded like a horse galloping across the sand. One night I was reading in bed when the book made a sudden jump. It took me a minute to realize it had been kicked by the baby. I waited, not moving, hoping it would happen again.

In March, when I was almost six months into the pregnancy, Hugh and I took a Saturday walk through Greenwich Village along with thousands of others who realized the smell of spring was in the air. We zigzagged along the narrow streets looking at the trendy stores selling leather dresses, futon beds, and exotic parrots costing as much as our used car. For supper we met up with friends at a Mexican restaurant, and took a window seat where we could watch the city move around us.

I surveyed the scene in front of me and idly wondered if this was what was meant by having it all. Anyone observing our table might have thought so. We were two young couples who had proved we could survive in New York City. The four of us were well-employed and could point to enough glamour and opportunity for advancement in our work to keep us going back for more. We were married, living in apartments that had character, and were no longer impressed by celebrities on the street.

In addition, I was aware that I looked exactly like one of the pictures in my pregnancy books. The sun was setting somewhere over the Hudson River while I sat by the window with both hands resting gently on my curving stomach. I also fit the role the media catered to: I had a husband, a career, and a baby on the way. To

advertisers, I was the perfect baby boomer—I was con-
tributing to the next boom. Even though I still toyed
with the idea that motherhood meant giving up my
freedom, I had to admit I loved the new life inside of
me. At that moment I was the image of the modern
woman whose biggest dilemma was how to find good
child care so I could go back to work.

Then came my March appointment, when the image
began to fall apart.

2 . Losing It

"**Y**our cervix seems a little soft," said the attending midwife as I attempted to read the fetal-growth chart on the wall behind her. "Perhaps we should look at a sonogram tomorrow and see what's going on." I waited in vain for further words of reassurance, but none came.

At the first mention of trouble, I have a habit of not dealing with it, but rather of stuffing the news into a corner of my mind. Meanwhile my heartbeat picks up, my stomach gets uneasy, and my palms grow sweaty while I look for a place to be alone and examine what I've been told. When I finally sit down by myself, I carefully pull the information into focus and begin to ask questions. Do I trust the source of the information, how bad is it really, and what can I logically do to handle it? I answer my own questions while coaxing my insides to calm down.

On my way home from the midwives, I stopped in the corner bagel place and took a window seat. After a few minutes of watching the passersby sort themselves into buses, subway entrances, and side streets, my mind finally settled down and I began to consider what I'd been told.

The evidence was not totally grim. I knew the mid-wife I had seen was reputed to be the most cautious concerning each detail of pregnancy. Her findings could easily be due to overconcern, and not a real problem in my body. I was a little embarrassed to realize I hadn't a clue what my cervix was, nor what it meant that it looked "soft." All I learned in the office was that if "soft" was the normal state of my cervix, it was all right, but if it represented a change, then something was happening and they needed to know what it was.

I left behind a half-eaten bagel and headed home, not really worried, just irritated that everything wasn't perfect. I was quite unprepared to handle anything out of the normal experience, and was more aggravated that something might be wrong than concerned over what it was.

I arrived at work the next morning with a cloud of unease circling the back of my mind. A soft cervix could be nothing, I reasoned while I was supposed to be thinking about promoting a condominium project in Greenwich Village. And it could mean real trouble, countered another small voice inside my head.

My abdomen did seem to tighten periodically as I sat at my desk, but according to my happy books it was probably Braxton-Hicks contractions (a kind of fore-taste of the real thing), or it could even be stretching ligaments, or maybe a stretching baby. To defy my own worry, I walked to and from my lunch appointment thirteen blocks away, reminding myself that walking was sensible exercise for pregnant women.

Most of my fellow workers were still out when I returned to the office and stepped into the women's room. It's amazing how many times a pregnant woman has to go to the bathroom. A minute later I felt my face grow hot, and heard the sound of my heartbeat in my ears. I stared down in fascination at my underwear filled with fresh blood. All I could remember about bleeding from the books came under the "Call Your Doctor Immediately" column. The small cloud of unease in my mind whipped into a tempest and I called the midwives' office from the nearest phone.

"Proceed to the hospital," said the voice, without hesitation. "One of us will meet you there."

"The emergency room?" I asked.

"No, labor and delivery." For a second I allowed myself to wonder if I were in labor, then slammed the door on that thought and picked up the phone again to call Hugh. I told him what was happening in as controlled a voice as I could manage. My voice becoming less controlled, I then explained it all again to Stella at the front desk, and rode down in the elevator fifteen floors to Park Avenue South.

Mercifully, Hugh worked several blocks from my office, and I could already see him coming up the street at a run, one arm outstretched to hail a cab. Suddenly I did not feel like taking one more step or controlling my facial muscles another second. The cab pulled up next to me, and I fell in next to Hugh, allowing the tears to fall as we turned off Park Avenue to head across town.

There are times in Manhattan when the traffic moves more slowly than a person can walk, and this was one of them. I slumped in the seat, trying to ignore what I suspected were not stretching ligaments, but, rather, uterine contractions gripping my stomach. Hugh and I said very little. He held my hand, and with my other I clutched the door handle, stifling a curse as every traffic light turned red against us.

How could the city continue, oblivious to my misfortune? We moved at a crawl through the flower district where ficus trees lined the sidewalk, and through the garment district where young boys wheeled racks of clothing across our taxi's path as if my life weren't falling apart in the back seat. "Run them over," I mumbled, becoming alarmed at the severity of the pain in my stomach.

We arrived at the hospital, and I realized this was how it was supposed to be: husband and wife breathlessly asking directions to the labor and delivery room, wife stopping in the hallway to pant through a heavy contraction. Only it's too soon, I reminded myself over and over. We're not supposed to be doing this yet. Not for another three months.

"Three months early!" Barbara exclaimed when she ordered me to the sonogram room. I hadn't seen Barbara since my first visit to the midwives, and was thrilled to find she was on duty in the hospital. If anyone could make logical decisions during this event, I knew it was she.

"We'll do our best to stop the labor," she said to me as I was wheeled toward the radiology wing. "But I don't know if we'll be able to." Before the sonogram I was handed a hospital gown, and my confidence fell even as my street clothes dropped to the floor. Barbara had indeed used the word *labor.* So I was in real labor, and that meant something was drastically, maddeningly wrong with this pregnancy. But what, and what could be done about it?

The sonogram, an image of my uterus projected on a screen, revealed that the placenta was not covering my cervix, a condition that could have caused the bleeding. Neither had the placenta separated from the uterine wall. I was in labor and my body was trying to deliver the child. Barbara ordered a dose of magnesium sulfate to slow the contractions, which were now coming almost every minute. They wheeled me into a room and began running the drug into my arm.

In half an hour I went from someone who had never been hospitalized to a patient hooked up to three machines. One graph with a movable needle registered the frequency and duration of my contractions, an amplifier recorded the fetal heartbeat, and the IV tube dripped drugs into my vein.

For a little while my body seemed to respond to the drug. The contractions slowed to every three minutes, and I pictured my body repenting of its horrible mistake and signaling the labor to stop and not come back again until July. Then the drug made me hot and drowsy, and I wanted to curl up and sleep until the danger passed.

Periodically an agitated nurse swept in to check all my monitors. "I just can't stand it," she finally said on her third visit. "There's a woman across the hall as pregnant as you are, only she's having an abortion. This is craziness." And she bustled out again, looking as if she might cry. I couldn't dwell on the irony; my contractions were growing stronger again, and seemed to be more frequent.

Looking up from my bed I watched a semicircle of faces form and re-form around me. Hugh was the constant. His hand never left mine, and peace seemed to flow through his arm and into my body as surely as the drug was doing. Whatever our marriage had been, I knew it was going to be different after this. "Don't you dare leave me," I whispered. "Not even to go to the bathroom."

Barbara was there also, silently collecting information and filtering it through her twenty-five years of attending pregnant women. A pained-but-practical expression stayed on her face as she watched the graph record yet another contraction.

A new presence entered the room, and I heard relief in Barbara's greeting: "Howie, I've never been so glad to see you in my life."

I rolled my head to one side and examined the new person by my bed. He was young, of medium height, with a neatly trimmed beard and thinning hair. Wearing a wool sportjacket and carrying a raincoat over one arm, he could have been a friend who had just happened to stroll down the hall. His eyes, however, were moving around the room ferociously, taking in every detail twice over.

"Who are you?" I asked bluntly, beyond caring about politeness.

"This is Dr. Howard Balick," Barbara said, then added with a laugh, "I guess he's Howie to me. He's our backup doctor, and I'm very glad to see him and get his opinion on what's going on here."

They exchanged conversation too low for me to hear, making frequent references to the monitors and my tightening stomach. I was aware they were discussing options, but I could grasp neither the basis of what was happening nor what needed to be decided. What I could hear, I didn't like.

"Has a twenty-four-week fetus ever survived?" the doctor said, and then answered himself: "Yes."

"Can it live without severe deficits?" Again he answered his own question: "No."

I tried to pretend he was discussing someone else's baby, perhaps a patient in the next room.

"If this drug works, and we can't tell yet if it will, then we've successfully stopped labor for the time being. However, the labor could start again, and we still don't know what caused it to begin with. Therefore you would have to remain in the hospital under observation to prevent labor from starting again, even if it means staying here for three months."

I must have groaned aloud because he studied me for a few seconds then said, "Actually, what we do is hang you upside down for long periods of time, which forces the baby to stay inside."

He gambled that I would respond to humor, and he won. It was the first relief I'd had since being there, and immediately elevated the man in my esteem. I could actually like this doctor, provided he didn't tell me something I couldn't handle, such as my having to spend spring in New York City in a hospital room.

"We need to decide whether or not to transport you uptown to St. Lukes," he continued, serious again, "where we are equipped to handle special neonatal situations." I did not need to look at the graph to know another contraction was on its way.

"Preemies need that care," he continued. "But if your baby were born right now," and he looked me right in the eyes, "its prospects for survival are poor, and even worse for ever being normal." There was no getting around this one. He was talking about me, and about the little heartbeat inside me that sounded like horses galloping on the sand.

He wasn't finished talking, and instinctively I knew I needed to lock my mind onto what he was trying to tell me. "I need to help you understand something," he said. "If this baby comes right now, we can go all out and take every measure to keep it alive. If you want to look back on this and say 'I did everything,' that is the decision to make. However, I strongly suggest less heroic measures because, if by some chance it does live and we put it on a respirator, you can't make any more decisions. Now if we can hold off labor even for another few weeks, the statistics improve. Unfortunately you're right at a critical point."

As the contractions intensified, I fought to think clearly and make decisions I could live with. My mind couldn't grasp lying in a hospital room for three months, watching a graph and listening to a fetal monitor. What would happen to Hugh, my job, my mind, under those circumstances? How did one pay for such a thing?

But what if I delivered now and the baby lived? Nothing in me could accept that alternative either. I simply could not imagine keeping a tiny baby alive who would never be normal, as an act of kindness or, worse yet, to comply with some medical regulation that couldn't be overruled. If I were going to deliver now, I didn't want it to live.

Suddenly my thoughts fragmented as my abdomen grew tight beyond belief. I heard my own voice somewhere off in the distance saying, "Ahhhh," and then the pressure released with a burst of water drenching the bed. The breaking of the water decided several questions automatically. Barbara did a quick examination and found my cervix had dilated three centimeters.

"You're going to have to have the baby now," Barbara said gently. "We can no longer try to stop the labor. This is it."

I looked desperately at Hugh. Have the baby? Not now. Please, some other time. Let me think about it first. Let me postpone this situation. It is absolutely the wrong time to have this baby. Besides, I don't know a thing about delivery. I haven't read that far in the books. And what does a six-month-old fetus look like? Whatever it looks like, I don't want to see it. I tried to recall the fetal-growth chart I had seen the day before, but couldn't pull it into focus.

As a nurse stuffed dry sheets under me, my mind strained to understand. I was pregnant, I was in labor, and I was going to deliver a baby—but there would be no baby. That was the bottom line. There would be no baby. What did I just live through for six months if there wasn't going to be a baby? This was a violation of my soul, a robbery of the worst, most intimate kind.

The faces around the bed were staring at me with some degree of anxiety. I realized they were waiting for me to react, to sob, or scream, or do something. But I couldn't. Hugh was the only one who knew me better than that. I'm not an immediate screamer. My reaction during a crisis is to become decidedly, doggedly calm.

I recalled with satisfaction my response when a car I was driving one rainy night spun out of control, whirling around and around on the slick highway. I sat calmly, my hands resting on the wheel, watching the scene that sped past my window. When the car finally slowed, I was in the right lane pointing in the right direction, so I continued driving homeward, ignoring the shocked faces in the cars around me. It wasn't until twenty minutes passed that my body began to shake so hard I had to pull off the road and regain my composure.

The woman lying quietly on the hospital bed was the same one whose hands rested calmly on the wheel of the spinning car. I smiled a little at Hugh as if to say,

"Don't worry, I'll fall apart later, when we leave the hospital. When I can do a really good job of it."

"We're going to give you a drug now to induce labor," Barbara was saying. "To see if we can't get this over with quickly."

My poor uterus. I pictured it still groggy from the first drug, which ordered it to slow down. Now it was receiving the signal to hurry up and get working. My body will be so confused, I thought as they changed the fluid running into my arm.

There was nothing to do now but wait. The room emptied, leaving Hugh and me to whisper together.

"This is different," he said thoughtfully, "from losing someone we know well, like our parents or a friend."

"This is someone who will never be a someone," I said, thankful to be talking to Hugh alone.

He nodded and continued, "At this stage it's more like losing an expectation or a dream."

I understood what he meant. "It's not as if it were going to be the president of the United States one day but now won't be, because after all, it just never was." I hoped Hugh knew what I meant, because I couldn't think how else to say it.

"I don't want them keeping it alive either," he said after a few minutes. "It would be better if it were delivered dead."

I was relieved that he said it first. "I don't even want to see it," I confessed. "Is that horrible of me? I just want this whole thing to be over with and to go home and put it behind us. I don't want to see what we've lost."

"It's totally your decision," Hugh said. "Don't let anyone make you do something you don't want to do. Knowing you, if you saw it, you'd carry that picture in your mind forever."

He was right. I only hoped I had the guts to stand up for myself. The medical staff seemed so sure of themselves, I never thought I would be able to control what was to happen. Thank God for this husband of mine who rarely let other people dictate his actions.

Barbara had warned us that my labor could go quickly, or take several hours even with our efforts to speed it up. We just had to wait. Hugh retired to the one chair in the room, a green vinyl affair designed for short visits, and I lay still, waiting to see what my body would do. I no longer kidded myself that I knew my body. Right now it was on its own schedule, and had decided for some reason to have no contractions at all.

During the lull my thoughts continued to churn. I was grateful Hugh and I were unified in our perspective. It gave me strength. We both accepted the idea that the pregnancy was over and there was no way we were going to have a baby. That alone gave us a certain peacefulness. Instead of a prolonged wondering if the baby would make it, we knew it wouldn't. It only remained to get through the delivery as quickly as possible.

I came to a resolution, and prayed silently for a delivery with no life. I wanted no hopeless efforts with tubes and machines and neonatal technology.

As I relived the last hour, I realized no one had offered an explanation for this loss. I didn't know why it was happening. One nurse had said to me, "It's hard to believe now, but you can always have another baby." But what if something were really wrong with me? Then I of course thought, what if I never can have another baby, and I began to cry just a little bit.

I looked up as a nurse came in the room, and followed her shocked expression to where my husband sat, sound asleep in his chair. "How can he sleep at a time like this?" she asked. "Doesn't he know what's going on?"

"Oh, he'll wake up when we deliver," I said, not having the energy to explain to the bewildered nurse what had taken me a few years to figure out. Under great pressure, my husband's body shuts down instead of revving up. The sleep was not a result of relaxation, but of extreme stress. We must look like such a funny couple. In a crisis, I grow calm and make flippant comments, and Hugh goes to sleep. You never really know how you're going to react until you're in the situation, and by that time you're beyond caring what other people think.

As I thought about Hugh and me, I realized my contractions were starting up again and there was no way to avoid what lay ahead. I couldn't buy or beg my way out of this. I had to give birth before I could move on.

"Are you all right?" Hugh asked. He had awakened and seen the needle jumping up and down on the graph.

"Of course," I stuttered. "But I want Barbara back in here now." I knew there was one thing that had to get taken care of immediately. The monitor next to me was faithfully recording the heartbeat of the fetus inside me, showing that it was still going strong. I needed that monitor turned off. I was certain this would end in death, and I absolutely did not want to know when it happened.

Barbara appeared within seconds. It was as if a silent signal went out from my room telling the staff my contractions were progressing with all seriousness. "Turn off the fetal monitor, please," I said, knowing I would do it myself if I had to. Barbara unhooked the contraption, seeming to understand the situation exactly. I was happy to relinquish myself to her care, confident of her ability to handle the situation, and glad not to have to think for myself. The contractions were coming faster and faster, taking all my concentration just to make it through each one.

"We'll move into the delivery room now," Barbara said, starting to wheel my bed toward the door.

"Please," I said, looking up at her face, "I don't want anyone to keep it alive." And I added, almost in a whisper, "Can't we just do this thing quietly?" Then the brightly lit delivery room came into view.

She never answered, but instead of turning into the delivery room where the nurses were readying themselves, I felt a decisive shove, and was wheeled right past it into a side room lit with one soft lamp. "We'll do it right here," I heard her say.

Just the three of us were in the room, Hugh's hand back in mine, and Barbara at the foot of the bed. My contractions were so strong they were taking on a life of their own. "You don't know when to quit," I said feebly, as Barbara examined me yet again. I knew my cervix needed to be dilated to a certain point before delivery.

Apparently she found what she was looking for because her next words were, "Okay, here we go. Now push."

"Now?" I gasped. "I don't know how. Barbara, I've never taken a Lamaze class." And then through clenched teeth, "I don't know what I'm doing."

"You don't have to; I do. Now push."

"Which way?"

"Be quiet and push." And several beats later, "Push again."

Still protesting I pushed down as hard as I could and felt the burning, overwhelming rush of a baby entering the world.

"It's a boy," I heard a voice say. "And it seems perfectly formed."

"And . . . ?" I asked.

"It's dead." There was a pause. "Do you want to hold it?"

"No," Hugh and I said in unison. And I watched her carry a small, blue body from between my legs, and out of my view. It was over.

Later that night I had a brief time by myself when my thoughts were clear, in spite of the emotion of the day. Barbara had warned Hugh and me not to make any decisions, and to make only the minimum number of phone calls, until we had time to accept what happened to us. I had finally released Hugh from my grasp so he could get a cup of coffee, and I lay quietly, thankful for the end of activity, tension, and decision making.

Those moments in the dimly lit room carried the same feeling as the wake of any great effort. I had lived through labor and delivery, and could sense the lingering exhilaration of pushing my body and mind to the limit. A certain peace pervaded in knowing that I had given my best to the situation.

The awful irony was that there would be no result for all my effort. I hadn't begun to deal with the loss yet, but knew instinctively what Barbara later confirmed. It would take time and being gentle with myself to figure out the whole mess. The shock and disbelief would have to wear off before I could start to make sense of it all.

Barbara seemed so in tune with our situation, and so able to read our needs, that many months later I went back to her office to ask for her perspective on handling women who suffered miscarriages and ended pregnancies.

I almost didn't recognize the woman in street clothes sitting stiffly behind a desk. She was far more at home in a white jacket, monitoring the progress of a delivery.

"First of all," she said, "there is evidence that 15 to 20 percent of all pregnancies fail, most in the first twelve weeks. No matter how far along, however, you're still dealing with loss, and that's hard.

"When a pregnancy ends that has progressed as far as yours, it's important for the medical staff to be slow and calm, and to allow the couple time for their reactions. You can't just whisk the baby away and expect the couple to be fine. It takes real sensitivity to their feelings. As medical practitioners, we've learned this over time."

She told me it was in trying to be sensitive to the parents that the practice developed of letting the couple look at and even hold the dead baby for a period of time before letting go. As Barbara said, "We try to convey to the parents that what they have lost is a tangible thing, and it's all right to take some time to say good-bye."

I have since wrestled with this issue, and come to some simple conclusions. For my husband and me there was no question: We did not want to see what we had lost, and have not regretted our decision. In speaking with a friend of mine, Debra, I saw the other side.

Debra is a nurse and had delivered one son with no difficulty. Her second child, however, was born at thirty-four weeks and was critically ill from birth. A little girl, she lived for six days in intensive care before dying. The medical staff handed the baby to Deb and her husband.

"I felt strongly about finally holding her," Deb explained to me. "It gave me time to say hello and good-bye, and to close the book. I only wish the staff weren't there because I could have sat alone with her for quite a little while.

"Some people absolutely cannot handle it, and shouldn't. However, if the medical staff makes it available, then the parents can choose. As a nurse, I've encouraged it because of my own experience."

Deb's experience, along with others I have heard, leads me to think that, ideally, the medical staff should allow the parents to make their own decision, alone and unhurried. Also ideally, the parents know themselves well enough to know what they can handle.

During my talk with Barbara, she wanted to make one emphatic point: "By far," she said, "the most important thing I can emphasize is that after a pregnancy loss there has to be a time for mourning, a time to go over events and accept them. It takes a while.

"Many times friends and family will dismiss the loss, especially if it's an early miscarriage before the pregnancy really shows. But the mother doesn't dismiss it. She knows what it meant to her, and she is aware of things no one else thinks about, not even her husband.

"Many times, for instance, she knows exactly when she would have started a childbirth class, quit work, or other important dates. She knows the due date for that baby. On those days, she's going to have a hard time; maybe she'll feel a wave of grief, or just cry for no apparent reason. Even her husband doesn't always know the dreams and expectations she built in her heart that have come to nothing. So a woman who's lost a pregnancy has to go easy on herself and allow some time to figure it all out."

That night in March when my pregnancy ended, Barbara performed one more heroic act in getting Hugh and me out of the hospital. I don't know if she understood I would heal better at home, or if she realized we didn't have medical insurance; but, for whatever reason, she left me alone for a only a brief time before returning to ask if I could stand up yet.

Barbara looked so resolute about getting me moving that I obediently teetered to my feet and let her and Hugh dress me in the outfit I had worn to work that day. Hugh settled me into a wheelchair and plunked my briefcase, which now looked like a foreign object, onto my lap. We were on our way. "It'll be easier at home," Barbara said as she shoved open the door and pushed me through.

We were an odd-looking entourage, gliding down the quiet hallways at 9 o'clock that night. We didn't stop at the front desk to explain our departure, but Barbara, with a commanding wave, steered me past the security guard and out onto the sidewalk at 9th Avenue. We bumped to the curbside where she hailed a cab and helped us into the back seat.

"The next time we meet here," she said through the window, "you'll be delivering at full term."

"Whatever you say," I answered.

"Thank you," said Hugh.

Twenty minutes later I was home in bed in the small midtown apartment I had left that morning, one lifetime and one pregnancy ago.

The apartment seemed strangely quiet and strangely welcoming. Immediately, I was glad we made the effort to get home that night. Facing the next day was going to be difficult enough without starting it off in a hospital room. Hugh made phone calls in the living room and I lay in bed staring at our venetian blinds, which were closed against the lights of Broadway.

I attempted to take inventory of my body, but could find nothing familiar. My curving stomach had disappeared, I ached from the waist down, and my thoughts raced in circles. My trusted body had betrayed me and I was stunned by it. Wasn't childbearing natural, hadn't billions of women since Eve done this thing successfully? What was the matter with me?

The stories about my mother, which had never meant a lot to me, suddenly became very important. The details I hadn't bothered to understand could be relevant to my life. Was it possible I had inherited her problems, and, if so, what exactly were they? What if childbearing would be an ordeal for me, and, if so, how difficult could it get before I finally delivered a baby at full term?

I had inherited my mother's enthusiasm for life, her determination, and her delight in adventure. My mother, who went to college during the depression, who was married ten days before my father went off to World War II, who joined the Navy to stay busy and became a pilot because they offered to train her; my mother, who started a business at age sixty-five and never thought she was doing anything remarkable, had a terrible time trying to have children.

Was my body going to give me a similar fight? Having a miscarriage twelve weeks into a pregnancy was not uncommon, but twenty-four weeks? How could that one be explained? Already I had moved completely out of range of any of my friends' experiences, and none of my pregnancy books began to deal with second-trimester losses. This experience had thrown me into the realm of "high-risk" pregnancies, which seemed a lonely and hostile place to be.

I understood I faced a battle, but this was the first real hardship of my thirty years and I wasn't sure how to handle it. This has been the longest day of my life, I thought as my eyes finally closed, and it won't surprise me if tomorrow is even longer.

3. The Royal Incubator

In light of the turbulence that marked the next few months, I'm glad my mother was the first person to visit me the day after the loss. She breezed in and out of our apartment one morning, leaving me with a new perspective on our family, an example of how to handle hard times, and hope for a happy ending. She also left me a little more grown up than when she arrived.

If I had expected her to dwell on the misery of my experience, I was disappointed. She cried with me briefly, both talked and listened at length, and left us food for several days. She didn't offer advice on how I could conduct myself in the situation, but, rather, she shared her experience from thirty-five years ago, and let me glean what wisdom I could. Over the coming months, I would decide that her attitude toward pregnancy loss was one I should adopt myself, especially as I became exposed to the alternatives.

I was awake for several hours before she arrived, and didn't anticipate her visit because my mind was completely disoriented. I had awakened that morning after my "spontaneous second-trimester abortion," and immediately tried to sidestep the disappointment awaiting me.

The phone was ringing but I didn't want to move. If I didn't open my eyes maybe I wouldn't have to think, and if I didn't think I wouldn't have to identify what was so wrong about the day. But, like Alice in *Through the Looking Glass*, the more I tried to avoid it, the faster I bumped into it. I wasn't pregnant anymore, there would not be a baby, and everything hurt.

Apparently I was "handling it well," as Hugh was telling someone on the phone in the next room. What constituted handling it well? True, I wasn't wailing, but not because there wasn't an enormous weight pressing against my brain, making it hard to think. The weight became familiar in the next few days, and I even labeled it "crisis." Later, I renamed it "tragedy." My heart held a dull ache, a constant reminder even when I wasn't thinking about *it*, that something in life was wrong. I wondered if the ache was permanent.

A generator roared into action in the courtyard outside my window, and I could hear the back doors of the Roseland Dance Hall swing open to let out the smoky air from the night before. These were sounds I woke up to every morning, but the shock of the day before had knocked me off balance, and I seemed to hear everything in a different way.

I stared at the still-closed blinds and wondered exactly how this situation would affect me, if my character would forever carry the imprint of loss, or if I would slowly move on and leave it behind. Judging from the dull ache, March 28th might become the focus of my life's calendar, a time from which to date everything else.

I could imagine myself saying, "Oh, that trip to Maine? That was before we lost the baby." Or, "Things were different then. You know, it was after March 28th, after we lost the baby." I supposed the event could so color my personality that I would become a sad person, one who always carried an air of distant hurt.

This brought to mind a woman I met at a surprise party, the mother of a friend. Attractive, accomplished, and now in her midsixties, she had raised two well-adjusted children. Soon after meeting her, with jazz music and laughter in the background, I heard about the baby she lost almost forty years before. She knew exactly how old he would be, what he might be doing, and what he would probably look like had he lived. Her eyes grew teary, and I couldn't think of anything to say.

Another woman who lived in our building still wore black in memory of her son who had died four years before. I had seen her in the elevator before Thanksgiving and asked lightly if she would be cooking a big turkey for dinner. "No reason to cook," she answered, and again I was speechless in the face of this massive sorrow.

I knew I did not want my life to appear so tragic that a Greek chorus could be heard as I spoke. I did not want to wear a cloak of sadness around me and make others uncomfortable by it. No, I would be a stoic. I would control myself and do my mourning in private. Only persistent digging would uncover the hurt in my life.

"There's someone who wants to talk with you," said Hugh, bringing the phone into the bedroom. I opened my eyes, took the phone and heard the voice of a longtime friend. She and her husband had been in our wedding party, had been in Manhattan to greet us, and had since moved out West with a new job offer. She was calling from Denver so I knew the word was out, circling at least as far as Colorado among our close friends and family. I was glad Hugh was there to monitor the phone calls.

"I'm just so sorry," Pam was saying. "Are you okay?"

The concern in her voice shot straight to my heart, releasing a rush of emotion. I opened my mouth to answer but nothing came out; my throat had tightened. It so took me by surprise I had to wave the phone to get Hugh's attention, and I handed the receiver to him before I cried into it.

Slumped in the bed with my eyes closed, gulping little breaths of air, I reevaluated the situation. So much for stoicism. There was a depth of emotion in me I hadn't anticipated. It was back to the beginning: How on earth would I handle this mess? What effect would it have on my life? Would I ever stop crying?

The buzzer sounded in the next room, indicating there was someone downstairs who wanted to come up to the apartment. Hugh hung up the phone and went to see who it was.

"Your mother is on her way up," he said returning. "I think she drove here."

Had she called and asked if I needed her to be there, I would have said no, but she was smarter than that and simply drove to the city. I pictured her leaving at dawn to cover the 200-mile drive by 10 A.M.

Then suddenly she was in the room, bending over the bed to give me a hug, and I cried all over again. This has got to stop, I thought in vain.

"I'm so sorry, dear," she said. Considering her own experiences, I knew she could have added, "I know just how you feel," but she didn't.

It had taken me until my late twenties to finally look at this woman as an individual, not an extension of my life. I even began to distinguish her characteristics as others must see them. Whatever her weaknesses, retaining past hurts was not one of them. As I was growing up, if she referred to her problems with pregnancy, it was in a matter-of-fact tone, as though recounting ancient history and not something she lived through. I realized I barely knew the details, and wondered if I had made up the parts I did know. Now, desperate to understand her experience, I asked for an account in detail.

She put down the plant she was carrying, checking the room for any sunlight that might have squeezed in by accident. She always arrived with a plant on the verge of blossoming, which had been carefully nurtured in her greenhouse at home. Two weeks in our apartment and it would become a brittle shadow of its former self, but she kept bringing stronger and stronger varieties, sure she would find one that could withstand the dry heat and perpetual shade of our three-room abode.

"It's hard to remember," she said at last. "We lost three babies, or, no, it was four. I forget sometimes because we've been rather pleased with the two we did have." She gave the plant a final nudge toward the corner of my bureau near the window.

This was a promising beginning. Here was a woman who didn't set her life's calendar around times of hardship, since she didn't even keep track of the exact times.

"Details, please," I pressed. "Did you lose any when you were as far along as I was?"

"Oh yes."

"In the hospital?"

"No."

"At home?"

"Not exactly."

"Well?"

"The first time was when we lived outside New York City, but we were seeing a doctor in Manhattan. One night I knew something was going wrong, and headed off in a cab to meet the doctor. It was a twenty-five-mile drive into the city, and I lost the baby during the ride to his office."

I remembered my own cab ride the day before, and shuddered. But it must have been earlier in the pregnancy for her, and maybe not so difficult.

"You were three months along?"

"No, five or six."

I could barely bring myself to imagine the pain, the contractions, the delivery somewhere on the Cross Bronx Expressway. I was already seeing my mother in a new light. Under questioning, she was revealing details I had never asked for before.

Her second pregnancy started well, and during the fifth month my father felt safe in leaving for Australia on business. When his plane landed in San Francisco for refueling he called home and found the second pregnancy had ended while he was flying west, leaving my mother alone to handle the affair.

"That one was difficult because I was so alone, and couldn't imagine what the problem was. Remember your father and I had been separated for two years during the war, and were so anxious to start a family. I do remember looking out my window at the people on the street and just wanting a baby so badly."

My mother's problem was not fertility, but being able to carry the babies to term. Pregnant for a third time, she learned my father's company was transferring them to the London office. Another woman might have hung back in the United States, to avoid the strain of traveling, and to continue with a doctor who knew her. Not my mother.

Three months into the pregnancy my father packed everything in the house and my parents moved to a second-floor flat at 192 Queen's Gate. They awaited the arrival of their furniture, including a grand piano, which came by ship at the company's expense. My mother was given explicit instructions by her New York doctor to find a specialist in the city and stay in bed.

While postwar London struggled to get on its feet, my mother thought about finding a doctor who would handle her case. She didn't know where to begin. Each morning she sat in bed reading the *London Times* to acquaint herself with her new home, and to keep up on the news of Dewey's campaign back in the States. Another news item caught her interest as well—the announcement of Princess Elizabeth's first pregnancy, which might produce an heir to the throne.

In one morning's *Times,* my mother read a letter-to-the-editor from Sir William Gilliatt, president of the Royal College of Obstetricians and Gynecologists, and decided to write him and ask his recommendation for a good doctor. He responded to the inquiry by offering to handle her case himself. Her search for a doctor was already over.

My mother reported to his office, and leaned back on the green horsehair sofa that served as an examining table. Looking up past Sir William's bushy gray eyebrows and stern expression, she saw hanging on the wall formal portraits of most of the female side of the royal family, hand signed, looking back at her. Not only had she found a specialist, but she had also stumbled upon the doctor who was attending Princess Elizabeth.

His orders were simple. My mother was to consume extra eggs and milk, and rest in bed as much as possible. Extra egg rations were hard to obtain, but the daily maid who came to their flat had a hen, and was interested in the extra money. Staying in bed was harder; the American woman wanted to explore London.

"I wasn't fearful of this pregnancy," my mother recalled, "because I believed this baby would make it. Your father and I prayed independently of each other, and both of us felt certain this baby was going to live. I gave up worrying about it."

Meanwhile Sir William took the country's interest in the royal birth as an opportunity to nudge the obstetrics profession from its makeshift habits toward more modern techniques. He was pleased by the arrival of a new automatic incubator, the first in England, sent as a gift to Elizabeth from the Isolette Company in Philadelphia. But he wasn't likely to test it for a while as the hospital staff was too wary to have it set up, and the Princess was experiencing a good pregnancy.

Not so, however, the American woman. On the morning of November 3, 1948, Sir William must have sighed when my father, the American businessman, called before breakfast to say that his wife was experiencing regular contractions. Still two months away from delivery, my mother had made it further than ever before. But she simply had to hold on for several more weeks at least. "I'm just having breakfast, but I'll be over," said Sir William, no doubt noting that Americans in general had poor timing.

Shortly after, Sir William climbed the steps to the American's second-floor flat, and surveyed the situation while the housekeeper peered over his shoulder. My mother lay in bed, where she was supposed to be. Next to her stood my father, sleeves rolled up, but otherwise dressed for a day at the office. Both of them were staring at a tiny baby dangling by its heels in my father's firm grasp.

This mental picture delights me now because I know my father well enough to understand how truly remarkable was the arrival of this child. Our family has joked numerous times that my father is a man of theory and intellect, not given to practical thinking. Nor does he have any interest in things anatomical. His doctoral degree is in economics, not medicine, and he soon veers away from any conversation with too much reference to the human body.

In college, when he observed an operation at Johns Hopkins Medical School, he retreated to the hallway to faint. This humorous, kind, and well-educated man has no interest in inspecting the details of how the body works, much less the desire to see the birth of a baby. Yet there was no one else around that morning when my mother announced in a low voice that the baby was on its way, forcing my father into the role of midwife for a premature, at-home delivery.

My mother had ordered a pamphlet, appropriately from the United States Department of Labor, which outlined steps to take in case of an emergency child-birth. As my father accepted the task at hand, she read aloud to him from the pamphlet, giving him instructions as the delivery progressed.

My father did have one medical reference in his brain, a picture in *Life* magazine of a doctor holding up a newborn by its heels, listening for the first cry of life. When his own baby arrived my father picked it up, turned it upside down, and waited.

As Sir William entered the room the baby chose that moment to let out its cry, causing the very proper doctor to drop his bag and take over the procedure, muttering about the "damned Americans." It was later rumored that solemn-faced, he had demonstrated this technique of baby-dangling for the nurses at the hospital, at the expense of my father's reputation.

After cutting the umbilical cord, Sir William sent the curious housekeeper off to boil water. He wrapped the baby in a pillowcase, and tucked it into a laundry basket for the ride to the hospital in a private car. My mother followed later in an ambulance.

At the hospital, the little boy was placed in an oxygen tent and fed predigested protein through a tube. My mother was wheeled into a bedroom down the hall and my father was sent off to his office where he could recover. Meanwhile, Sir William set round-the-clock nurses to watch the new baby.

It was one of these nurses, Sister Josephine, who the next week found herself following Sir William to Buckingham Palace. She was to be the night nurse

for Princess Elizabeth, who had just given birth to
His Royal Highness, Prince Charles Philip Arthur
George.

In time Princess Elizabeth heard about the tiny American baby struggling to live in a specially humidified
room at the hospital. At under three pounds, he had
little chance of survival, and indeed that week his
condition deteriorated.

Sir William came to my mother's room to prepare her
for the worst. The infant wasn't digesting food, and his
breathing was labored. In a letter home, my mother
described the situation:

"The baby took a real tumble today, and the doctors
(whom I could hear running down the hall) shook their
heads. From the first Sir William has been pessimistic,
and—as a good Church of England man—has been
urging us to have the baby christened in the hospital.
He doesn't want the baby to slip away without the
proper blessing.

"But after a long talk with the chaplain, we decided
not to, knowing that we had dedicated this baby to God
from the beginning and were confident he would live.
We didn't want to haul down our flag."

So they continued to hope and pray, and the baby
began to breathe regularly.

About that time, Elizabeth saw no reason why the
American baby couldn't be put in the "royal" incuba-
tor, and in no time the tiny boy was enclosed within its
Plexiglas walls. Although skeptical, the nurses accepted
Sir William's instruction on how to use the new con-

traption and word spread about the unusual machine and its tiny occupant.

When the press heard about the event, three London newspapers arrived to record the story, and equipment appeared to make a newsreel. By the time the cameras rolled, someone had hoisted a small American flag above the machine in tribute to the determination of the small life within.

My parents were able to forewarn their families about when the newsreel would run in the United States, and both sets of grandparents were able to see their new grandson courtesy of Fox Movietone.

With so much support, the baby, now named Brian, was obligated to survive and began to improve steadily. Sir William said Brian could leave the hospital when he reached five pounds and, on Christmas Eve, after an extra large dose of food, my parents finally brought him back to the flat where it all started almost two months previously.

When the baby went months later for his first vaccination, the pediatrician mumbled something about using the same needle on Brian he had used on Prince Charles, no doubt thinking these Americans could use all the help they could get.

This miracle baby would be my only sibling. Of course he later turned into the brother who tormented and teased me mercilessly, in spite of his royal beginnings. Nevertheless, after a good many years of fighting, we became the best of friends, and I'm grateful for the now Queen and Prince Charles and the royal incubator.

My parents stayed in London for four years, during which time they had another premature baby, who lived for a brief while before dying in the hospital. After their return to the States, they moved to a house outside of New York City, and my mother went to Columbia Presbyterian Hospital for another try at understanding what caused so many problems in her effort to have children.

A surgeon at Columbia Presbyterian performed an operation in which he found a small wall of tissue dividing her uterus almost in half. He removed the tissue and felt her ability to carry a baby to term was greatly improved. From one viewpoint my mother was fortunate. She had no problem getting pregnant. She only had a problem staying that way long enough to have a healthy baby. Perhaps the operation would make the difference.

I lay in our tiny New York apartment listening to my mother's voice and remembering the enormous house I grew up in, which rambled across a hillside and had enough bedrooms and bathrooms for five children. I had reigned uncontested over the house and back-yard woods, oblivious to the drama my parents lived through in order to give birth to me. It was in that house that my mother became pregnant again, soon after the surgery, and had an early miscarriage.

"I hardly remember that one," she was saying. "It was so early into the pregnancy."

As my mother recounted the story to me, I began to see that an early miscarriage for her was relatively insignificant after losing three other pregnancies so far along. For another woman, one early miscarriage could seem like the end of the world.

In 1954, pregnant for the sixth time in ten years, my mother was ordered to bed for the duration. She and my father moved into the guest room on the first floor of our house, hired someone to take care of six-year-old Brian, and prepared for the long haul. At seven months along she was moved into the hospital where the doctors could keep an eye on her. When nothing happened, they finally let her go home and finish out the pregnancy in her own bed.

Except for trips to the bathroom, she obediently kept to her bed. At full term she took one middle-of-the-night trek to the bathroom and felt something unusual. Returning to the bedroom she immediately gave birth to me, once more forcing my reluctant father into his midwife role. That was probably the last straw for him because, afterward, they decided two children was enough.

"After you, we stopped trying," my mother concluded. "We had our two, and have been rather glad we did."

I found myself staring at the new plant, and then beyond it to where my mother sat precariously on the heater cover because there was no room for a chair in the bedroom. She still looked like my mother. There was the same copper-colored hair swept off her face with combs and the same green eyes. She wore one of the outfits she'd sewn from a Vogue pattern book, and a simple necklace purchased in some European village she and my father had discovered during their travels.

Other than that, nothing was familiar. It was the first time I realized that what had been a family tale had really happened, and for the first time I was experienced enough to understand the implications. I had lost one pregnancy in the safety of a hospital. She had lost four in far worse places. The enormity of what my parents went through to have two children was staggering.

I finally made one of those startling, yet utterly obvious connections that are part of growing up. Whereas up until now I saw my life as the focal point of my own world, it was obvious my mother had had her own experiences, which predated mine, and which were just as much the focal point of her world. Suddenly my life fell into place as one in a long series of generations. My mother was recounting her experiences to me, and before long I would probably be recounting mine to my own daughter. But what if I never had a daughter? If I inherited my mother's insides, who knew what it would take for me to finally have a healthy child?

The idea of never having children is attractive to certain couples, and I questioned if we could be one of them. Didn't I have a wonderful husband, and wasn't that enough? If I ruled out pregnancy entirely and put my mind into my work, I could build a career exciting enough to keep me going for quite a while. Hugh and I could make enough money as a double-income couple to travel and live in an apartment with sunlight. On weekends we could go out for a lengthy brunch and tinker over the Sunday crossword puzzle without having to think about babysitters or booster seats.

Hadn't I spent most of my pregnancy in denial, working as if nothing else were going on in my life? Didn't I look with pity at mothers who had to be with their children all day and talk nonsense, or worse yet say nothing but "No" over and over again while the kids reached for boxes in the grocery store? It would be a simple step for Hugh and me to plan on a life without children.

As I considered this, a funny thing began to happen. The more I thought about not having children, the more sure I was I wanted them. What a fool I had been to take pregnancy so lightly and concentrate instead on things that didn't seem so important now. You could take the dumb job with its urgent meetings and priority memos and expense account lunches. You could take my apartment, and the entire island of Manhattan if you wanted, just let me have a baby.

Then my throat began to knot up again, and I could feel despair creeping into my mind in the form of a thought I kept trying to beat away: What if I tried everything to have a baby but never could? The disappointment might crush me. Was I looking at a lifetime of misery?

Yet, here in the bedroom was a woman who lived through four losses, most in her second or third trimester, and yet carried no misery with her. Instead she concentrated on the two children who made it, and she stayed thankful for what she did have rather than being bitter about what she had lost.

As far as I could see, her ability to pray and believe in the face of all negative evidence actually changed the circumstances around her. The strength of her conviction mobilized a royal doctor, an automatic incubator, and a Princess's blessing to save the life of her son. And all of this when medicine was over thirty years less sophisticated than today. Who knew what resources I might also mobilize if I kept the right attitude?

My mother reached over and automatically resettled the plant into the one beam of sunlight that lit our bedroom each morning for a few minutes. Then she stood up, pushed her hair into place and said, "Okay, I'm going to put together some lunch. Someone around here needs to think about Hugh, who's probably a little bit hungry by now."

The subject of pregnancy loss had just closed for the morning, and I began to get the picture. Sorrow was allowed, but not self-pity. I could cry all I wanted, but not wallow. Life might be painful for a while, but I needed to keep moving and not give up. I could see a clear choice in this matter. For me it would either be a Greek chorus in the background, or a Princess with a miraculous incubator.

Hugh joined my mother in the kitchen, glad to see a real meal taking shape. I was alone again, telling myself it was time to grow up. "You know," I spoke out loud to make sure I got the point, "it might not be easy to have a baby, and it might get worse before it gets better. Pull yourself together, hoist up your flag, and fix your mind for the battle."

4 . Thawing Out

One thing about a state of shock is that you don't know you're in it. You know something terrible has happened, but you don't feel anything. Everyone who speaks to you asks how you are, and you say you're doing fine because you don't know what else to say. In this numb existence you can take care of details, make decisions, and go on living because absolutely nothing is real to you anyway. You can't really believe the terrible thing happened, because if it happened you wouldn't have lived through it, and here you are living.

Shock set in when I saw blood come out of me in the women's room in my office. A woman in her twenty-fourth week of pregnancy isn't supposed to bleed, much less in a Park Avenue office building. From that moment on, I watched events through a haze of disbelief. All my ideas of how life should progress were being overruled by my own body, and I was out of my league.

I'm sure there are people who withdraw during a shock, or those who sit motionless waiting to feel again. I am not like that. My job required hours and hours of digging up information and organizing it. Right after the pregnancy loss, still in my numb state, I automatically began to dig and organize. I didn't know what else to do, and I couldn't bear to do nothing.

I set up my base of operations in the living room. Wrapped in a terry cloth robe, I sat on the couch and spread my weapons on the coffee table before me. To one side were my happy-pregnancy books. Although they had betrayed me, I could use them as a reference. To the other side I set my phone and address book, a notebook, and a cup of hot tea.

My intent was simple, and my mind focused. I wanted to know one thing: *Why?* Why did I lose the pregnancy? Knowing the answer wouldn't bring back the baby, but it would help me get a handle on what had happened.

My plan was simple. I would start by looking up miscarriage in the index of each book and read the list of causes. Then I would call Barbara and the young doctor whom I'd met while in the hospital. After that, I would phone everyone in my life who knew something about pregnancy and childbirth, searching for clues to my own situation.

I found most of my books in agreement that one in six pregnancies fail, and that of those, 75 percent end in the first twelve weeks. Causes include genetic abnormalities, hormone imbalance, infection, environmental toxins, and blood incompatibility between the mother and fetus. Information was scarce concerning losses such as mine that occur after the first trimester. Accidents involving a blow to the stomach, diabetes, malnutrition, and problems with the placenta were all listed.

I considered the list of causes and didn't see anything that seemed to apply to me. If it were something as abstract as environmental toxins, I was no more at risk than any other woman in New York City. I had been well-behaved concerning not smoking, drinking alcohol or caffeine, and making sure I exercised. I didn't have an infection or diabetes, and the sonogram had shown no problems with the placenta. Could it have been the morning I climbed fifteen flights of stairs to my office?

After all my reading, I was no closer to a solution. My books offered no more clues, and I couldn't march off to a library in my terry cloth robe and look up miscarriage. There was one question I knew only Barbara could answer. I wanted to know if the fetus had an abnormality that might have caused the labor. It was time for a telephone call.

I asked Barbara's office to page her at the hospital, and waited, hoping I would be able to keep my voice steady when she called. Her call told me what I suspected already. The fetus appeared perfectly normal, so much so that they felt an autopsy wasn't necessary.

This information quieted one of my concerns, but raised another. If I hadn't caused the miscarriage myself by something I did or didn't do, and if there was nothing wrong with the fetus, then there must be something wrong inside of me. Something from within must have gone wrong and caused the early labor.

Barbara reminded me that my cervix had appeared soft the day before the loss. She could not confirm, however, if my cervix had thinned out because labor had started, or if the thinning cervix had caused the labor. Which had come first?

She suggested I talk with the doctor who had been at my bedside and ask his opinion. "We won't be able to follow your case now," she told me. "This loss makes you a high-risk patient and, as midwives, we aren't equipped to care for you under these circumstances.

"However, give Dr. Howie Balick a call and see what you think of him. I can tell you this much about him. He's good at what he does and he'll take time to talk with you. After that, you decide."

I felt lonely indeed when Barbara ended the conversation. Here was the medical person who stood by me during my whole ordeal, whom I trusted and wanted to stay with, but now I was out of her league also.

Wondering more than ever what could be the matter with me, I immediately phoned Dr. Balick's office. I knew he had tried to explain some things to me in the hospital, but I had been in no condition to understand them. Now I wanted to know it all. He talked with me briefly on the phone and set up an appointment for a week later when he could answer my barrage of questions in his office.

"I want to know now," I said irritably.

"Why not give yourself more than twenty-four hours to figure out the entire workings of your body," he suggested. "I'm not going anywhere."

"I might," I said to myself, thinking of wandering off into the wilderness and not coming back.

Driven by a sense of immediacy, which I couldn't even explain to myself, I went through my address book looking for people in my life who might be able to tell me what had gone wrong with my pregnancy. There was no logic to my search, simply the overwhelming desire to find the cause of this disaster.

Under R I found one name I wanted, Dr. Carolyn Rawlins. This woman is a legend of sorts, a pioneer in introducing natural childbirth to the Midwest. In forty-one years of practice she has delivered 15,000 babies, enough to populate a small town. When I last knew of her, she was practicing at St. Margaret Hospital in Hammond, Indiana, but frequently taught and lectured in other areas of the country.

I had experienced the range of her intellect, wit, bluntness of speech, and tremendous concern for people when I interviewed her for an article many years before. At that time I was objectively interested in her viewpoints. Now I desperately wanted to hear her opinion of my own case.

I phoned the number not knowing if she still worked there or if she'd even remember me. If she would take my call, I didn't know what I'd say, and I was dimly aware that she might not answer me because she wasn't the doctor involved in my situation. I dialed the number quickly so I wouldn't have time to talk myself out of it.

Not only did she remember me, she took my call and treated me to a brief blast of her concern and experience. She confirmed for me that most miscarriages happen in the first twelve weeks, and it was rare to lose a fetus after that.

"I've seen two major causes for loss after the first trimester," she said. "Both of which we're able to handle better than ever before. The first is a weak or incompetent cervix. How's yours, by the way?"

Again I realized how much I didn't know about my own anatomy. I told her that one of the questions in my case was which came first, labor or the thinning cervix.

"Are you a DES baby?"

"Yes."

"Then look for an incompetent cervix. We're finding a lot of cervical problems in you babies whose mothers took DES. I prescribed the damn stuff myself in the fifties; thought it was wonderful. Now we're seeing some bad results."

I confessed I didn't understand what she meant by incompetent cervix, and she explained. "If the cervical structure is weak," she said, "then the weight of the growing baby could be enough to force open the cervix, causing labor and premature birth."

"What do you do for it?" I asked, finally able to pin down a possible cause of my own misery.

"Get stitched up."

I waited for more.

"You know, like a purse string. Once you're pregnant, we put stitches around your cervix, pull them tight, and then cut them when you reach term."

I was ready to fly to Indiana that afternoon. "Would I have to come to your hospital?" I asked.

"No, silly. Get some doctor in New York to do it. Wait a few months and get pregnant again. Then get stitched up, go to term, and have yourself a baby. Good-bye."

"Wait, what was the other reason for premature births?"

"Problems in the uterus. But we can go in these days and have a look around. Never could do that before."

"Do you think I can have a baby?" I asked, feeling like a baby myself.

"If you believe you can. Good-bye."

I hung up and considered this new information. This is it, I said to myself. I've got the reason I've been looking for. My cervix is weak, and it's not a big deal to fix.

I was astonished at how much comfort I found in having a possible answer to my problem. Not only that, Dr. Rawlins was so matter-of-fact about my loss, as if she saw this sort of thing all the time. Maybe I wasn't the only one in the universe with this problem, but one of many who faced the same situation.

I wondered how Dr. Balick would react to my self-diagnosis. Then I remembered that, in the furor of the hospital visit, he also had said something about a weak cervix, which meant nothing to me at the time. Life looked brighter already. All I needed to do was get pregnant, get stitched up, and have a baby. I was ready to do all of this right now. If I got pregnant immediately, I reasoned, it would almost be as if this loss never happened.

The phone rang, and I picked it up with a new lightness in my heart. It was Patti, my sister-in-law. She is married to that miracle brother of mine, and happens to specialize in obstetrics. She has assisted in hundreds of births and even teaches classes on pregnancy and childbirth. I gave her a brief account of my weak-cervix theory.

"One thing you may find," she said gently, "is the urge to get pregnant immediately to retrieve what you just lost. Don't. Give it some time. Your body needs time to return to normal, and your heart needs time to heal. You've received a big blow, but you probably haven't registered it yet. Take it slowly."

I appreciated her advice but didn't believe it for a minute. From my command post on the couch, I began to lay out plans for my life. Desperate to be able to control a situation that seemed overwhelming, I planned my future as I thought it should happen.

Hugh wandered by and took in the picture of me surrounded by my books, notes, and phone numbers.

"Are you working it all out?" he said with a glint of humor in his eyes.

"Don't you laugh at me," I warned. "It so happens I do have it all figured out." And I poured out in one breath all the conclusions of my research.

"First of all, I probably have a weak cervix, which means I'm weak down there and can't hold the baby in long enough. It happened because my mother took DES, but that's okay because they can sew me up the next time and the baby won't fall out, so what we need to do is get pregnant right away, find a doctor, and that's not hard because I think I've found one, and he'll stitch me up, and then everything will be all right, because they'll cut the stitches after nine months and we'll have a baby."

Hugh just stared at me, so I kept going.

"Now, Patti says I need to take time to heal emotionally, but I don't think that applies to me because I'm okay, aren't I, I mean, I'm not falling apart or anything, and this must be as bad as it's going to get, so I'm probably ready to start again soon. I know what's wrong with me, so we can just take care of it and move on."

He kept looking at me with the kindliest expression on his face, not saying anything. I know that expression now, because I've worn it myself while listening to women in similar situations, babbling from adrenaline, disbelief, and a state of shock.

Even as I explained how fine I was, I had no idea what my body had in store for me. While I raced through my books and phone calls, my body continued on its own agenda and came to its own conclusions. It had given birth, but didn't know there wasn't a baby. Right on schedule, in full force, my milk came in.

That afternoon I awoke from a nap to find that, where I used to have a modest-sized chest, there were now two rocks. My cervix might not work right, but obviously my breasts had no problem. They were going to make up for the rest of me.

Stumbling toward the kitchen, arms hugged around my chest, I found Hugh and cried without restraint.

"Lllllook what happppened," I stuttered, pointing at my expanded bust line.

"Whoa," he took in a breath, and for once had no comment.

I stumbled back to the bathroom and pressed until the milk came streaming out, relieving the pressure.

"It can't be helped," said Barbara when I reached her on the phone. "Whatever you do don't be tempted to press out the milk. You'll only stimulate more production. There is a pill you could take, but believe me the side effects can be more unpleasant than what you're experiencing now. Try an ice pack and a tight bra."

No ice pack has been designed for this particular problem. In a daze, I put ice cubes on our kitchen counter and began pounding them with a pair of pliers. I gathered the chips into a plastic bag and anchored it all to my chest with a giant bath towel I tied behind my back. No shirt fit around this new bulk; only my bathrobe would stay wrapped. I couldn't stay upright or the whole contraption slid down to my waist, so I returned to my bed and stared at the ceiling.

Of all the injustices, I thought. This is the worst. I can't have a baby, but I have enough milk to feed six babies. I can't stand up, can't relieve the pressure or I'll bring more pressure on top of it. I remembered a dairy farmer who told me how uncomfortable cows get if they're not milked. That's it, I moaned to myself. I'm like a lonely cow locked out of the barn.

I learned later that the milk was just evidence of tremendous activity in my body. Hormones were flying, my uterus was still contracting, and my muscles still ached. When there's a baby to nurse and care for, these natural physical reactions can be endured. In the absence of a baby they can be intolerable.

The discomfort strained my already fragile equilibrium, and I started plunging in and out of despair with astonishing speed. I could be talking to Hugh, clear-eyed and calm, and suddenly cloud over with tears and overwhelming sadness.

As the hours went by, Hugh developed finely tuned radar. "Hormone attack," he'd say and hug me once more until the sadness passed.

"Everything seems so, so, so hopeless," I tried to explain. "I hate this. I hate feeling this way."

"It's that mothering hormone," clucked Patti when she called again that night to see how I was doing. "There's a study I read about that someone did on dogs. They extracted this hormone from a female dog who just had puppies. Then they injected it into a male dog."

I could count on Patti for the medical perspective. "What happened?"

"He stole the puppies from the female. Pretty powerful hormone."

"No kidding. I'm miserable."

"You've got nothing to mother," she replied.

I thought about this for a moment. At least there was some physical justification for the way I felt. "I'm not going crazy?" I asked.

"Certainly not. On the contrary you're very normal. You can be thankful your body works this way. When you do have a baby you'll have no problem producing milk."

"It seems like I'll never stop."

"You could be a wet-nurse."

"I want my own baby, thank you. I just don't know what to do with myself right now."

Relief came in the form of two friends of ours who called with a suggestion.

"We're going out of town for a week. Why don't you come stay in our apartment while we're gone. It'll be a change of scenery, and you can hide out from the world. No one needs to know you're here, and you can take some time to get on your feet."

It was the smartest offer anyone could have made. This couple lived in a huge apartment compared to our own little shoebox. On the top floor of a brownstone, they had skylights, both southern and northern exposure, and sliding doors onto a rooftop terrace. I had learned, like all city dwellers, to place a premium on sunlight. I noticed that even long after people leave Manhattan, they gravitate toward windows as if it might be their last glimpse of the sun. This apartment was so bright the furniture had faded. Hugh and I were thrilled.

Just getting out of our apartment was a relief. Everywhere in my home were reminders of my pregnancy:

bottles of vitamins on the kitchen counter, queen-size panty hose in the bureau, flat-heeled shoes and big skirts in my closet, and a pair of baby booties hanging on the mirror in anticipation. We shut the door on all of it.

I burrowed into the new apartment as if I'd never leave. We put on the answering machine to screen phone calls, and I curled up on the couch in the sunlight, wrapped in my robe, with the ice pack anchored to my chest.

It was in this environment that I began to come out of shock into the full realization of what happened. My friend Debra had described her own experience with this, and I remembered her words:

"At one point I began to thaw and it was like emerging from the ice age. I looked around saying, 'what the hell just happened to me?' I could finally think, and feel, and piece things together."

I emerged from my state of shock in the full sunlight with Hugh coming and going, and no obligations to see anyone or talk on the phone.

After two days of not letting Hugh move out of earshot, I didn't mind his going off to work for a while. As long as I could reach him by phone I felt safe. I couldn't remember ever needing someone so badly before, and was shameless in my demands for his attention.

Like a little kid, I went through the perverse enjoyment of once again drinking coffee, eating a double-fudge brownie, and having a glass of wine—all of which I had denied myself for months. I read magazines, listened to music, and entertained long, involved thoughts about life and what was really important to me.

For hours at a time I stayed on an even keel emotionally, especially as my milk receded and I recognized my body again. I picked up my diary with its previously spotty entries and wrote page after page about what happened. Writing it down provided an unexpected relief. I had needed to stand far enough back from the incident to find words to describe it. Distance gave me perspective.

The rooftop apartment became a halfway house between my troubles and the world I would need to re-enter. I hadn't expected to be afraid of getting back out on the streets, but every time I looked out the window I was thankful to be safely above it all. I felt so fragile and raw that the simple movement of people on the sidewalk might blow me over.

Sitting above it all on the little terrace, I could look down on peoples' heads and nurse my mind back to health. When I was ready, I began to talk with friends on the phone, and some even came to our hideaway to spend a few minutes on their way home from work.

I realized later that the shock of the situation had emptied my mind of the trivial clutter I was accustomed to carrying around. My life came to a momentary standstill, which afforded me time to look around with new eyes. My mind became a sensitive instrument registering peoples' comments, everyday situations, and my own emotions in strong relief.

During the initial months after the loss I made a mental list of others' responses to my situation, trying to figure out what encouraged me and what dragged me down. I wanted to remember what effect the words had so that someday I might be able to encourage other women in the same circumstance.

In general, there were those who avoided me and those who tried to say or do something to express their sympathy. When I walked past our doorman for the first time in my unpregnant state, he couldn't look me in the face, but ducked behind his counter as if searching for a lost package. When I first returned to the office, a week after the loss, there were those who made a wide arc around my desk for several days at least. I didn't blame them. I know how awkward it is to face someone who has gone through a particularly difficult time. I just wanted to tell them, "Hey, I'm no more comfortable with this whole thing than you are. But avoiding it doesn't make it any easier."

A reaction that puzzled me came from women and men who had children of their own. Time after time they would look at me with tremendous hurt in their eyes and say a simple "I'm so sorry to hear what happened." It wasn't until I had my own child that I realized why. People with children knew what I had lost. At the time I only understood something was missing, but I didn't know what it was. They understood, and could hardly bear the thought.

Inevitably after a pregnancy loss someone says, "It's okay, you can always have another one." I did not know if I could have another one, and found no comfort whatsoever in that comment.

Another comment left me speechless: "Well, it just wasn't meant to be. That was nature's way of not allowing a damaged baby to be born."

I understood that, in the first twelve weeks of pregnancy, the body may abort a fetus with a genetic abnormality, and it can be considered a blessing. In my case, however, there was nothing wrong with the fetus, but in my ability to carry it. I knew that baby was meant to be, and we had been robbed of the joy.

Overall, the outpouring of cards, phone calls, and kind gestures was overwhelming. I felt totally undeserving, yet thankful for each one. I know it takes some time and courage to communicate with a person in need, and I told myself again and again to remember how much those gestures meant to me, so I could be there for someone else when they needed it.

Many people made brief calls to express their sympathy and ask if there was something they could do. I could never think of anything. Finally I realized there was something people could do. Several times friends called and allowed me to talk about what happened. As they listened patiently, I related the details of the loss, how I felt, or what I expected for the future. When someone let me stumble through an explanation of my feelings, it allowed me to understand them better myself. They may not have known all they did for me by letting me put into words what was so hard to comprehend. But each time I explained the event, I saw it more clearly, and put a little more distance between it and me.

One category of response provided the most comfort. When a woman with a similar experience took the time to talk with me, it provided deep and instant companionship. To be able to talk with someone who had lived through it was comforting enough, but if her story ended in a success, it was invaluable.

As with any hard time, my experience inspired people to tell me either their own stories or the account of someone they knew. Every victory story of a woman overcoming odds to finally have a baby boosted my expectation and belief that I could have a victory also. I could not hear enough of them, and was amazed at how many there were to hear. It seemed that every woman, or her mother, or her friend had a miracle to recount and a solution to recommend.

My natural-foods friends had stories to tell of women who stayed away from sugar and white flour, ate plenty of fresh foods, and drank gallons of raspberry leaf tea, which is supposed to be good for the uterus. They all gave birth to big, round-cheeked babies who cooed happily and never had colic.

A woman I knew in California had lost several pregnancies. She would have contractions without knowing it, and go into hard labor before the doctors could try to stop it. Finally she was given a belt to wear that monitored her uterus during pregnancy. At the slightest sign of a contraction, a device on the belt registered it, and she could get to the hospital in time for them to prevent labor. She had her new baby in tow as she explained how it worked to me.

From all sides, I began to meet women who had their cervixes stitched up throughout their pregnancies. A neighbor of my parents had two children running around her legs as she described to me how successful it had been in her case.

I heard stories of miracle pregnancies, and miracle births, and miracle babies who made it against all odds. I began to get the idea that a woman's body is naturally in favor of childbirth, and babies naturally fight hard to live.

One of my favorite stories came from a business associate. He sat at his desk on the thirty-fourth floor of a new office building and told me about a woman he knew who tried for years to get pregnant with no success. She, her husband, and friends went to Radio City Music Hall one night and during intermission she stayed in her seat while the others wandered off. As she looked at the giant curtain on the stage she saw a vision and knew God was telling her she'd have a baby. The vision was so clear to her that when the others returned, she asked if they could see it too.

"Well?" I asked. "Did it happen?"

"Yes," he replied. "She was my mother."

No matter what the story, I added it to my list of ammunition to help me believe I could have a baby. I knew much of my battle would be in keeping my mind peaceful. As Dr. Rawlins told me, I could have a baby if I believed I could. I pictured myself sitting in Radio

City, wearing a belt from a hospital in California, and drinking raspberry tea. I wanted my own victory story.

The nature of my ended pregnancy lent itself to a quick recovery, at least physically. Labor and delivery were relatively fast, and my body bounced back easily. Because our baby did not live even a short time, Hugh and I had no prolonged stay at the hospital waiting to see if the baby would make it. Within several days after the loss, my body was already calmed down, and my mind working again. However, I was still reluctant to leave my cocoon in the sunny apartment, not trusting my wounded emotions to stay in check.

It was work that finally pried me from my nest and showed me how life kept going in spite of my problems. One week after the loss the office manager called me in my hideaway. "I hate to ask you this," she said, "but we've got to send out a proposal and need that project description you were working on. Did you leave anything on your desk we can use?"

I was surprised to hear myself answer her clearly, and to remember almost exactly the outline of the document she wanted. Apparently that part of my brain continued to function even though the rest of me had been to the moon and back in a week's time.

I found myself agreeing to stop in the office, if only for an hour or so, to take care of the most pressing business.

"By the way," she said before we hung up. "I've taken the liberty of telling some people what happened so you won't have to explain it over and over again."

She did a good job because when I did return to the
office, no one said "Hey, what happened? You don't
look pregnant." I never had to explain because they all
knew.

Two weeks after I lost the pregnancy, when I had
been back at work for about a week, a small incident
occurred that let me know I was moving on. My firm
became involved in an enormous real estate develop-
ment. Someone put up the money for a party to bring
all the partners together and celebrate the proposed
deal. They reserved a private room in a restaurant to
entertain the politicians, money people, developers, and
investors. My presence was expected at the event.

The idea of going to a party seemed ridiculous to me.
I had barely even smiled in two weeks. An evening of
people congratulating themselves over a real estate deal
seemed so trivial compared to the deeply personal events
of my own life. Surely anyone who looked at me would
instantly read disaster on my face. I anticipated drag-
ging myself to the restaurant dressed in my work clothes,
slipping in unnoticed to find the few people I was
obligated to talk with, and quickly escaping to the
safety of my home.

On the afternoon of the party I left work to stop at
home before the event. On my way I looked in the
clothing stores near my office and thought about my
looks. Spring was in the air, but I was still in winter
clothes. I was wearing one of the big skirts I had bought
for the pregnancy, only now it was loose and I had
safety pins gathering it at the waist. My regular clothes

were still too tight, and, anyway, appearance was the last thing on my mind.

Looking at my reflection in one of the windows, I could see the bulky pleats and uneven hem caused by my halfhearted attempt at alterations. Perhaps I had time to find a simple outfit for the evening that didn't make me look as depressing as I felt.

I ended up buying the first thing I picked off the rack, and hurrying home to put it on. The new dress inspired me to fix my hair and put on eye makeup. By the time I left the apartment I was late, but looked better than I had in two weeks. The eye makeup helped; I just had to make it through the evening without a sudden rush of tears to spread it across my face.

Instead of arriving early, I made it to the restaurant when a sizable crowd had already gathered. There was no way to slip in unnoticed, and I felt the focus of the room momentarily turn to me as I came through the door and took off my coat. From the first I knew something was different, but it took a while for me to figure it out.

Few people in the room knew me, and therefore believed only what my name-tag said: Director of Corporate Communications. They were treating me like a woman having fun at a party, not like an emotional wreck. It had been almost seven months since I was a working woman, instead of a pregnant woman who was still working. These people thought I was normal!

I found a corner from which to observe the room, and a man next to me took it upon himself to point out all the bigwigs in the crowd and tell me how he knew them. I resisted the temptation to interrupt him and say, "That's interesting. I just lost a baby and feel like a deflated balloon flapping in the wind." As long as he couldn't read tragedy all over my face, I might as well let him keep going.

I stayed longer than I expected to, and actually forgot the pregnancy for several minutes at a time. When I heard myself laughing at a funny comment, I knew I was on the road again, inching away from the loss and moving ahead. It would be a slightly different life than the one I knew, but at least I could see forward movement, and that was encouraging.

5 . Hugh

I deally we're always growing in our marriages, but a crisis can speed up the process. The effort to have a baby strained my relationship with Hugh in ways we might not otherwise have experienced for years, and showed us things about each other that might never have been revealed.

My immediate reaction to the pregnancy loss was a fierce need for my husband, which leveled any walls that stood between us. It left me clinging to him, uncomfortable if he was in another room for a few minutes or tried to go downstairs to the mailbox. Jobs, daily routines, and irritations melted into insignificance compared to the overwhelming need for his presence and comfort.

Recently, I recognized similar feelings in another couple, Mark and Joanne, who lived in our building. We saw them mostly in the hallway in the evening on their way home from work, but knew little about them. One day I learned they were finally pregnant after a long time of trying. Soon after, I met Mark in the hall during the middle of the day, and heard unaccustomed passion in his voice. Instead of talking about work, he told me Joanne had a miscarriage.

"I could care less about going to work," he said. "Work is nothing, the rent is nothing, the bills are nothing, and I don't care if I get fired. What really matters is each other." And he hurried down the hall toward his apartment.

I realized I, too, had learned that what I really have in life are the people I love and who love me, and that other things pale in comparison. The hard part is remembering it on a daily basis.

When my desperate need for Hugh finally abated, we were faced with the day-to-day realities of our relationship, and how to live with each other in the aftermath of a personal crisis. That's when I stopped taking my marriage for granted, but saw what it really means to me to be married to Hugh, and how much work it takes to keep it healthy.

Over time, three lessons stood out to me about my marriage. All three were things I could have known anyway, but the drama of the pregnancy brought them rushing to my attention. The first lesson: My husband would always be the same man I married, only more so. Like many wives before me, I thought my husband would change over time. I didn't realize that a person's basic nature rarely changes. The crisis didn't give either of us a different character, it simply revealed more of what was already there.

At the time I did not yet understand this, nor did I know my husband well enough to guess how he might react to the events in our lives. Actually, it took quite a while for me to want to know what he was going through, because initially all I thought about was myself.

It is natural after the loss of a baby for most of the sympathy and concern to center on the woman, with her husband receiving little if any attention. It was certainly that way in our case. Flowers arrived at the door for me, the phone calls were to inquire about my health, and the concern was mostly for my state of mind and my physical recovery.

It took my father to point out the obvious. He phoned one evening several days after the loss to see how we were doing. Before we hung up, in his understated tone that I had come to respect, he said, "Honey, how's Hugh holding up under all this? It's hard on him, too, don't forget. Take care of him."

I recognized the voice of experience speaking and glanced over at my husband. I had been so wrapped up in my emotions, and hormones, and fluctuating body, that I hadn't thought about Hugh having a hard time. I didn't have a clue what he was thinking or feeling, and didn't know if I wanted to know.

I grew more concerned as I considered the possibilities. Hugh hadn't said anything about himself or how he was faring. He had been quietly attending to our lives while I lay in bed. He looked in control, but what if he were in inner turmoil? In my fragile state, I wouldn't be any help at all.

Or what if his silence came from thinking his wife was a failure because she couldn't carry a child? I'd never be able to live with that kind of pressure. Or what if he were shocked by how upset I'd been, and wondered why he married such an emotional wreck? What if he turned into something totally different from what I knew up until now? What if he left me because I couldn't have a baby? What if, what if . . . ?

We had only been married a year and a half but had known each other for several years. I tried to think what I really knew about this man, looking for clues as to how he might react under these new strains. This was the first real crisis we had faced together, and I knew it had the potential either to bring us closer or cause real problems. Our personalities were different enough on a normal day that extraordinary pressure might send us reeling into opposite corners.

I looked back to when we first met, far from the cosmopolitan air of Manhattan. Our relationship sneaked up and took me by surprise when I lived miles away from my familiar life and familiar future plans. Knowing I would eventually settle down with a predictable, safe husband, probably a lawyer, I enjoyed the novelty of Hugh's friendship. This dark-haired maverick piqued my curiosity. I never expected he would walk into my heart and make himself at home.

Our relationship started in the mountains of northwestern Montana, where it was dangerous to admit having even visited New York, much less having lived there. I had gone to Montana as part of my spiritual quest. I wanted to know what would happen if I trusted God to provide for the needs in my life.

I couldn't honestly perform the experiment in the midst of the material abundance that surrounded me. It was too easy. Growing up in a suburb of Manhattan, I went to fine schools, had endless possessions, and numerous lessons, practical and otherwise, such as French, tennis, skiing, piano, riding, and ballroom dancing. My town, Rye, and my education, Ivy League, were the sure route to a profession somewhere in the belly of New York City, twenty-five miles from home.

My life was falling into such a well-worn groove that I needed a drastic detour before I lost forever the willingness to learn, explore, and be flexible. With 200 dollars, I arrived in Missoula, Montana, thinking that by the end of my experiment I would be either very wise or very cynical.

My year in the wild northwest provided so much dimension for my life that, even when I landed back in my well-worn groove, it was with a permanently altered viewpoint. For the entire year I had lacked for nothing, but, rather, had watched finances, friends, work, and adventure appear exactly when needed. Most important, I ran into countless people whom I helped, and who helped me.

Almost secondarily, I gained a solid respect for mountains, rivers, storms, and the endless sky, which existed whether I was looking or not. And I respected the ingenious people who ran their own businesses, built their own homes, enjoyed activities like jumping off cliffs in hang gliders, and jealously kept their lives a secret from the rest of the country.

I was introduced to two people who became my companions in this adventure, both of whom had gone to Montana for reasons similar to mine. Abbie, a fearless redhead, was braver and brasher than I was, and taught me that just because I'd never done something was a lame excuse not to try.

One night we drove to a mountain hot-spring during a snowstorm and sunk our bodies in the warm water while snowflakes melted on our faces. On a warm day we rode horses into town, and left them tied to a fence while we went for drinks at a hotel and listened to "Moonlight in Vermont" on the jukebox. We hitch-hiked through the mountains, skied, learned to dance the two-step at cowboy bars, placed a heater in our car engine and plugged it into the garage when the temperature dropped, and picked cucumbers when we wanted to experience an outdoor job.

We woke up each day with little idea of what lay ahead, but that's the nature of a spiritual quest. So with one raised eyebrow we dared each other to look beyond our physical circumstances and trust God for work, and housing, and people, and situations where we could give or help.

Hugh was our other companion, and it was during this unusual time in my life that he and I developed the peculiar relationship that I never could explain to myself.

Abbie and I often drove into the mountains to watch the progress of a geodesic dome house rising in a secluded valley. Hugh was one of the crew building the house for the owner, who was part hippie and part politician. At lunchtime we all sat on the unfinished porch to eat avocado and sprout sandwiches and stare at the sky. Periodically, elk paraded across the ridge behind the house, paying little mind to the strangers trying to claim their territory. Lunchtime conversations were about the governor, rattlesnakes, the world economy, and skiing conditions.

Hugh didn't say much, so I called him the silent cowboy. He drove a clean, white pickup truck, wore a leather jacket, and loved working on the house. Sometimes he'd explain the theory behind the dome or how solar energy works, and make me question what else I hadn't learned in Rye, New York.

Over several months, I formed a picture of his past. He wasn't a silent cowboy, but a silent southerner from a family of engineers. He quit college after three years of engineering, taking his own journey away from formal religion, social expectations, and the job waiting for him in his hometown. On the surface I saw very little we held in common, but respected what I glimpsed under the surface, and began to save up bits and pieces of ideas to share when we next talked.

One day I borrowed Hugh's truck to take to town and, when I returned to the parking lot, found a jagged black gash on the formerly unmarred white cab. The guilty party had fled without leaving a note, so I drove slowly back to face Hugh with the damage.

"It's okay," he said simply after a glance at the door.

"You're not upset?" I asked.

"It already happened," he said as if explaining to a simpleton. "You can't change it now."

That was the last I heard about it.

At Christmastime, Hugh scoffed at Abbie's and my longings to make it a special occasion. Abbie confessed she was the former chef of Abbie's Diner in West Springfield, Massachusetts, and began baking loaves of cranberry bread. I wrapped presents, wrote cards, and bought candles for the house. But as the day approached, we felt more keenly the absence of our families. I got mad at Hugh because he didn't seem to care.

On Christmas morning we heard an unfamiliar motor in the driveway and looked outside to see Hugh in a fancy black Jeep. He herded Abbie and me into the back of the four-wheel drive vehicle, throwing the cranberry loaves in behind us. Then he drove up and down the snowy roads, making stops at the homes of people we had come to love. At each house, we delivered a gift and were invited in for hot drinks by the fire. Instead of being a disappointment, that holiday set my standard for what Christmas should be.

Hugh, with his knowing brown eyes and nonchalant air, alternately infuriated me and endeared me to him. He was unimpressed with what I called my credentials, yet constantly challenged me to have confidence in myself and try out what I wanted to in life instead of dreaming about it. I couldn't manipulate him into my court, but always found him there when I stopped trying.

At his urging, I submitted an idea to a magazine and got an assignment to write about a professional baseball team practicing in Montana over the summer. Part of the "Pioneer League," these eighteen-year-old boys, fresh from high school, had been shipped off to the mountains for their introduction to the major leagues. I saw them lined up at a pay phone trying to reach girlfriends in Oklahoma, and recognized a good story. My only problem was ignorance about baseball.

When the professional coaches arrived from Florida to review the team, I was invited to sit in the bleachers and get my information. "Give me a quick overview of the sport," I urged Hugh the night before.

He shrugged. "I don't know that much about it."

"Well think of something," I pleaded. "You got me into this." He was not only unsympathetic, but amused by my problem.

I went the next day thinking I could learn by watching. Instead I found myself hopelessly confused by the activity on the field, and unwilling to admit my ignorance to the coaches.

"Understand any of it?" said a voice next to me. It was Hugh, stopping by on his lunch hour to see how I was doing.

"Not one thing," I said miserably. "What are they doing out there anyway?"

"Lou can help you," he said, and pointed to a friend of ours balancing himself a few seats above us. "I brought him along. He used to coach college ball." Hugh left me in Lou's care, and disappeared back to work.

I filled my notebook with Lou's careful explanations and vocabulary, and handed in my story on time. When it was published I showed it to Hugh.

"This is amazing," I said. "It came out okay, and I knew nothing about baseball when I started. Thanks for the help."

"What's your next story?" was all he said.

Hugh and I started jogging together on Saturday mornings, but never on a normal route. I followed him up unpaved roads, into the hills above town, where we could see the splendor of the valley and the mountains beyond. Hugh would always tease me that I couldn't run very far, so I'd run farther to prove him wrong.

On these long runs Hugh would sometimes start to talk about himself. It annoyed me that he would reveal himself after I had no breath to ask questions or comment in return. I had to be content scurrying along next to his loping stride, trying to log what he said for future reference and at the same time watch my feet that I didn't disappear over the edge of a precipice.

"What motivates you?" I managed to gasp one morning when I thought he was vulnerable to questioning.

There was no answer. "It's not applause," I tried, hoping to prompt a response. "Or money." Still no answer. "Or peoples' opinions of you." Silence. "What do you want out of life, anyway?"

"Maybe you can figure it out," he said.

And I will, I thought as he picked up the pace, preventing any further talk on my part.

As our relationship grew more constant I puzzled more and more about what drew us together. I, the born diplomat, was with a man who didn't know how to cushion the truth. I cared so much what people thought of me, and he didn't know what it meant to care. I wanted to talk everything over, he was content with thinking.

I realized from the beginning I did not resemble the sexy, free-wheeling females who seemed drawn to Hugh's side. "I guess I'm not the kind of woman you're used to," I ventured one evening when we met after work. Any man over eighteen could have recognized this as a moment to say the right thing.

Instead he said, "I've been with some very beautiful women. Maybe that's why I don't care about looks." I was stunned. Couldn't this man invent a compliment for my benefit? Apparently it was not within his nature to say the convenient thing. He did not fit my picture of romantic, but he did win my trust. Again, I didn't know whether to be insulted or grateful.

After much analysis I concluded Hugh was smarter than I was, or knew how to make me think so, which had the same effect. He was trustworthy, unresponsive to direct questions, contrary, a good problem solver, incapable of doing something just to impress someone, stubborn, and not visibly emotional.

Our being together was so unlikely that I forgot to guard myself against it. I found myself talking to him about things that meant the most to me, and enjoying his perspective. I gained respect for his way of thinking, and then began to care about whether he cared about me. When I started thinking about the future I knew I was in trouble but wouldn't admit it. There were so many reasons we shouldn't be together.

As the summer approached, I only knew I depended on Hugh's companionship but, after that, I was on unfamiliar ground. What happened to the East Coast girl who was going to marry a lawyer? Here I was thinking about a rebel with no profession, who drove a truck and wore cowboy boots. My predictable life was melting away in the Montana sun.

In June, when the daylight hours lingered long into the evening, Hugh and I were both invited to a friend's house outside of town. The graceful wood and glass structure sat at the top of a hill surrounded by trees. The party inside celebrated the end of cold weather and the advent of water-skiing, hang gliding, and camping.

I found my way to the rooftop terrace and saw Hugh had found it before me, and was already looking over the balcony at the treetops. While I watched, he swung one long leg over the railing, and stepped out onto a small ledge. I leaned over to say hello and he motioned for me to join him.

"You're nuts," I said, looking at the way the hill dropped out of sight beneath his feet.

"Maybe," he said, "but the view is better from here." And he sat down, dangling his legs over the void.

Something inside told me if I put my foot over that railing it would change my life for good. I hesitated, waiting for the inner voice to tell me to stick to the safety of the terrace and forget about ledges and men who sit on them. But it didn't. I climbed over the railing and sat down. Pushing my back hard against the railing, I opened my eyes and saw the woods spread out beneath me with a river glinting periodically through the trees. Hugh was right, the view was better.

We were silent for a time until Hugh spoke, his eyes still on the scenery below.

"So, we'll get married."

It wasn't exactly a question, but it wasn't a declaration either. It was more an admission. While I searched for the right response, he went on talking.

"I wonder who designed this place?" he mused. "I like the idea of one central living room with all the other rooms spinning off."

"I'd like," I said carefully, "to return to what you said before."

"That we should spend our lives together?"

"Yes."

"I agree," he said.

"No," I countered. "I mean yes that's what I want to talk about."

For once, he looked genuinely off balance. "What's there to talk about?"

I thought very hard about my objections, about being from different backgrounds, about college degrees, careers in New York, and children who take piano and ballroom dancing lessons. I knew if I started talking I could kill the relationship right there.

And if I did, I'd fly back to New York and drop
straight into some office where I could find a secure job
and whoever the man was in corduroy pants and loafers
who lived in a comfortable groove. And it would be the
end of my companionship with Hugh.

"This is a marriage proposal," I said to myself, wondering why reality is never like the fantasies we hold.
"So why don't I know what to do?" It was basically
simple. From the outside, everything about our being
together was wrong. From the inside, it was right. I had
to decide which to believe.

Part of my mind said, "This could be what you've
been looking for." Another part said, "But you better
take the safe route and say no." Then the realization:
"You waved good-bye to the safe route a long time ago.
You're kidding yourself if you think you can go back."

"Okay," I finally said out loud.

"Okay, what?" Hugh said. "What are you thinking?"

"I'm thinking that I'm sitting here on this ledge with
you, and that says it all."

Typically, we didn't speak again, but sat there looking at the view before climbing back over the railing
and joining the party.

It was a long time before we finally married, and
throughout that time I was repeatedly amazed by our
differences and then comforted by our companionship. I
loved what I understood of Hugh, but found myself
equally surprised by things I didn't expect. The ultimate
irony was his suggestion that we live in New York City.

The embarrassment was his getting a job immediately as a job supervisor for an architect while I floundered for four months. He never broke stride in the move from mountains to high-rises.

When I finally met Hugh's family, his mother gave me her version of his nature. With a voice still accented from her childhood in the low country of South Carolina, she warned me what I was getting myself into.

"Stubborn," she said, pulling a pitcher of tea from the refrigerator. "That boy will argue with a stop sign."

She filled a glass with ice and poured. "He'll drive a point into the ground and break it off." She smiled fondly. "Why, he can annoy you so much you want to shake him."

"Alison," she said putting the glass in front of me, "he won't do what you want him to, and he'll forget to say he loves you, but he'll love you so faithfully it'll make your head spin."

So, I had a partial picture of the man before I married him, which became a lot clearer when we were in the turmoil of the ended pregnancy and our character traits were waving in each other's faces. In the months after the loss, while nursing my wounds, I saw clearly that the parts of Hugh that either distressed or impressed me in Montana were the same ones that distressed and impressed me in New York City. Time and location hadn't changed the man.

Even though it's illogical, I find many women want their husbands to react to a pregnancy loss in the same way they do, with the same intensity and at the same time. A wife may feel betrayed when her husband expresses his grief differently, brings it up less often, and seems to recover faster.

I was spared these misunderstandings. From the beginning Hugh and I were outwardly so different that I never expected him to react the same way I did. Mostly I wanted his love and patience while I worked out my own peace of mind.

What I didn't expect was an education in my husband's character and our relationship. It was as if the crisis brought out all our strengths, weaknesses, and peculiarities for each other to see. Even today, our problems arise from the same few issues I saw then, and the same solutions still work.

I learned, for instance, that my husband doesn't tolerate "what if . . ." questions. He simply refuses to consider how our pregnancy might have turned out if only I had waited for the elevator instead of taking the stairs to my office, or researched DES-related problems before getting pregnant, or arrived at the hospital an hour sooner.

No matter how I brought it up, he wouldn't fall for this line of thinking. I should have known. This was the same man who, looking at the damage done to his truck in the parking lot in Montana, said, "It already happened. You can't change it now."

Hugh and I have always expressed ourselves differently, and when I allowed him his way instead of trying to change it, our lives were smoother. Basically, I express myself verbally, with drama, and very often. Hugh often looks like he doesn't care, shies away from discussions of feelings, and says less and less the more deeply he's affected by something. His deepest feelings sometimes surface in an entirely different situation from the one that caused them.

Several months after the pregnancy loss we were out with some friends, and climbed into a taxicab together as an angry-looking woman got out of it. It took us a few seconds to realize the driver had refused to take the woman to her destination outside the city, preferring to pick us up instead. We all knew this was illegal, but Hugh called the man on it. The driver, already defensive, started yelling at Hugh to drop the subject. I watched in awe as Hugh took on his most determined look and slowly pulled out a pen to copy down the cabbie's ID number.

Within minutes the event escalated. The driver, furious at the prospect of being reported, pulled the car to a stop in the middle of the block, got out, flung open Hugh's door, and tried to strangle him. The rest of us ended up on the sidewalk, our friends screaming for help, watching the driver try to kill my husband, who was going to copy down the number at all costs.

After mediation from several passersby, Hugh ended up on the sidewalk with us, and the driver pulled his cab into the 9th Avenue traffic and disappeared. Later on when we were all safely home, I wondered to myself what had prompted my husband to push so minor a disagreement to the absolute limit, with determination out of all proportion to the situation. The more I thought about it, the more I figured I knew the answer. My behavior of late hadn't been so temperate either. I knew better than to bring it up, and let the incident slide away in silence.

Concerning the pregnancy loss, I was the one who continued to mention it. I recognized so many dates concerning the baby if it had lived, that I was forever realizing something was missing. When Hugh arrived home from work I might greet him with, "Well, today was the beginning of our childbirth classes," or "I would have been eight months pregnant this week." And, while he always listened me out, he rarely discussed it or brought up the subject of his own volition.

In a moment of clarity, I looked back on our relationship and realized Hugh's conversation was no indication of how much he cared about something. The Christmas in Montana when Abbie and I pined over the lack of holiday feeling, Hugh had laughed at us. But he was the one who borrowed the Jeep and gave us a day to remember.

Even his marriage proposal had taken up as few words as possible, but he hadn't wavered one inch on his commitment since that day. I had thought an outward display of feeling indicated true caring, but maybe I needed to look a little deeper.

This was a revelation to me, and one that made more sense the more I thought about it. I began to look for how Hugh expressed his concern rather than wondering why he didn't react as visibly as I did. I came to understand that my husband tries to find solutions rather

than talk about the problem. He doesn't enjoy asking why it happened or what might have been done to
prevent it, but rather finds relief in having something
he can do now.

After the loss I noticed all the baby paraphernalia we
had collected disappeared from view without my thinking about it. Somehow Hugh quietly packed it away
where I never found it. I also noticed him quietly
protecting me from reminders of pregnancy or helping
me face them. At one party, he stood between me and
an especially enthusiastic pregnant woman. At another
time he heard of a woman who just lost a pregnancy,
and practically forced me to talk with her to see if I
could offer some help.

Other women, too, have found that the time after a
pregnancy loss is especially revealing of their husband's
nature. My friend Debra remembered: "While I continued to ache inside, and bring up the loss in my conversation, my husband virtually disappeared into the office
and began working harder than ever before. And he's
always been a hard worker.

"On a normal day, he holds things inside, but he
buried this one so deep it took a crowbar to get it out. I
kept getting angry with him for not being as sad as I was
or wanting to talk about it. I thought he had forgotten
it. Then I realized he was working out his unhappiness
in the only way he knew. I had my way, and he had
his."

Other wives told me of their need to talk about the
loss, their continued tears, and frequent bouts of sad-

ness. Meanwhile, it seemed their husbands played tennis for hours, worked on a project in the basement, or painted the house.

In the months following our first loss, and even more so after the second, Hugh and I rarely discussed what happened to us, and when we did, it was in brief spurts of conversation. I could have discussed it for hours, and often did with other people, but that's not my husband's way of coping, and I respected that. I also knew his silence did not come from indifference. I finally recognized and believed in his concern without hearing it from his lips.

I became content with simply telling him when I was passing through a time of sadness or anger or discouragement, and learned to take comfort from his presence and his listening ear. I could ask for compassion and patience, but not for a different husband.

The second great lesson I learned in my marriage was to focus on what I had, not on what I lacked. This principle works in all areas of life, but is vital to a marriage. As with most simple principles, it is easy to understand, and requires more work to apply.

When I was still lying in the hospital, only hours after the loss, a man called me whom I greatly loved and respected. A spiritual man and a teacher, his works had inspired me for years. Eventually I made his acquaintance, and countless times thought of his example when I faced a difficult or perplexing situation.

I don't know how he heard about my plight or found the hospital name and number, but shortly after I was wheeled into the small recovery room, a phone rang beside my bed. Out of habit I picked it up. Immediately I recognized the voice, which sounded older in the year since I'd seen him. He didn't say much, and I was too numb to understand what he meant, but in later months I found his words coming back to me over and over again.

"You knew my heart would go out to you at this time," he began. "Look for something greater to come out of all this." Then he paused. "And stay thankful."

"Thankful!" I wanted to yell, "What do you mean thankful?" But the conversation was over, and I never spoke with him again because he died soon after. It wasn't until I saw the results of unthankfulness that I understood why he said it.

In the many women I began to meet who faced pregnancy loss, I recognized a tendency to focus unyieldingly on not having a baby. When I allowed the thought of the baby I didn't have to dominate my life, all I noticed around me were pregnant women, children, and maternity stores. Instead of enjoying what I had, I ached for what I didn't. It is a rare marriage that can hold up under the continual strain of something missing.

Focusing on lack breeds bitterness. I saw women whose bitterness over not having a baby colored their whole personalities and caused them to lash out at their husbands. In some cases the bitterness had grown so deep that even when the woman went on to have a baby, her heart was too hardened to enjoy it.

The only antidote I learned to this was to make myself thankful. When I felt that life was unfair, and I wanted to take it out on Hugh just because he was there, I learned to stop and talk to my mind in stern tones.

"What are you thankful for?" I'd say to myself.

"Nothing," I'd answer sullenly.

Then I'd get tough, "Listen you ingrate, aren't you blessed with two arms, two legs, good eyesight, a healthy heart, and a good mind? Well? Do you have two wonderful parents who care about you? How about a roof over your head? Nice clothes? Enough skills to get a job? And how about your husband? Think of all the people who are depressed because they're alone in the world, and you not only have a husband, but a wonderful husband."

Instinctively I knew no matter how patient Hugh was, I could drive him from me if all I thought about was a baby. He might not leave me physically, but he would leave mentally if I become a sour woman. Remember, I told myself, to be more thankful for Hugh than desperate for a baby, or you'll wind up with neither. I was blessed to have a marriage worth appreciating, and the more I realized it, the less likely I was to ruin it with bitterness.

That led me to my third lesson, which was that a marriage worth appreciating takes time and effort to appreciate. One morning in our borrowed apartment a few days after the loss, we sat down to breakfast together. I put a vase of fresh lilies on the table, and found matching place settings and cloth napkins. We set plates of croissants, peach jam, and sliced pears to one side. Freshly ground coffee dripped into the coffeepot, and our cups stood ready on the counter next to a pitcher of cream. Hugh slid open a window where the sun was already reaching into the living room, and we found peaceful, morning music on the radio.

As soon as we sat down together I realized how long it had been since we'd done anything like this. We both worked nine-hour days and saw each other for about three hours. The deep conversations we had before marriage had disappeared. Our mornings began now in two different directions with each of us headed for the subway, and a coffee and muffin from the 8th Avenue Deli.

Something had slipped, but I didn't even realize it until we sat down and I remembered how much I loved it when the two of us were alone and didn't have to be somewhere in the next ten minutes. Here I wanted a baby so badly, but wasn't caring for the one relationship already in my life.

"This is it," I vowed to myself. "Every day I'm going to set the table, and have fresh flowers, and use half-and-half instead of milk."

"I doubt it," argued my more realistic side. "You'll be back at the 8th Avenue Deli in a week."

Perhaps flowers and croissants weren't the answer, but I could see effort was required to keep our marriage from being mere coexistence. Time, communication, and thoughtfulness would be key ingredients. It didn't matter which of us made the first move, we needed to put more life into the relationship.

Since then I've been both successful in my effort, and negligent, but never again deluded into thinking my marriage would take care of itself.

After our pregnancy loss, one concern about Hugh I harbored for a long time was that he secretly felt angry at being deprived of a son. I felt bad enough about losing the pregnancy, and I wondered if he didn't resent it in his own way too. One day when we were passed the initial drama of the incident I asked him how he felt.

Not really banking on a response, I was surprised when he answered. "I'm very glad," he said thoughtfully, "that I'm not a woman. I don't think I could have gone through all that."

Then I understood something else. He really, truly wasn't hurt for himself, he was hurt for me. I thought for the first time what it must have been like for him to see me connected to IV tubes and monitors, trying to control myself through the intensity of labor. And then living with me during the changes in my body, and getting used to being unpregnant again. Hugh wasn't hiding inner resentment, he was concerned for me.

A few months after the loss I learned something else about Hugh that made the next few years a lot easier. We had been given the gift of a weekend in Vermont by my parents. They suggested we go away for several days after all the excitement and sorrow had died down and life had settled into a routine again. "That's when you'll need it most," they said wisely.

I found a bed and breakfast place on a mountain road, and we made it our base for three days and traveled out from there around the state. The Vermont spring was cool, and a damp wind whipped the branches of the still bare trees. We took the time to drive through small towns and stop where we liked. We rode horses at a nearby stable, and ate leisurely meals. Our conversations centered around the places we visited and the people we met, never once around babies and loss.

As we drove home down I-95, I thought about trying to get pregnant again, and what would happen if we tried and failed. Hugh loved kids so much. I didn't know how I'd react if we had another failure, and his disappointment on top of it could be devastating.

It was dark and a little bit rainy, and we drove for a long time in silence, watching the rhythm of cars passing and slowing, and passing each other again. Out of nowhere, Hugh spoke as if he had heard my thoughts out loud.

"I don't care if we never have a child," he said. "I'd be very happy being just the two of us. We don't have to have a kid you know. If you don't want to try again, it's okay with me."

"I thought you loved kids," I said.

"I do. But they don't have to be mine."

"Honest?" I asked, but he didn't answer. I looked out the window and realized I had to believe him. After all, this was the man who had never said anything just to make me feel good.

If Hugh didn't care, then I was free to try again
without the pressure of his disappointment. All I had to
deal with was my own. If I couldn't have a child, then I
knew at least Hugh would be able to live with it. Okay,
I could go for it again knowing my marriage didn't hang
on its success. I thought maybe now I was ready.

6 . My Back to the Wall

By two months after the first loss, my body was back to normal and the event was no longer ever-present in my mind. Other than the sting I felt every time I thought about it, I was able to nurture a bright outlook and regain my sense of humor. As I had been warned, the grief came in waves, which eventually lessened both in frequency and intensity.

My great desire to move on helped me to do so easily. I didn't want to dwell on the event. I didn't want to be depressed and bitter, and I didn't want a pregnancy loss to ruin my life. I was more than willing to return to normal and leave the shock and grief behind.

In addition, a commitment I had made before the pregnancy loss rose up and claimed my attention, and I gratefully threw myself into it. I had agreed to help with a theatrical performance produced by volunteer labor. The hours and hours of focused work provided a way for me to exhaust myself and feel good doing it.

On the medical front, Dr. Balick performed a hysterosalpingogram, which allowed him to view dye as it passed throughout my uterus and tubes. He was looking for another sign of DES exposure—a malformed uterus. If present, the malformation could be so severe as to make the uterus heart-shaped, or so slight that only a small dip across the uterine roof could be detected. The test revealed only the subtlest of malformations, not worthy of surgery.

In some ways I never fully dealt with my pregnancy loss, but succeeded in putting it quickly behind me as an example of a freak event. In the back of my mind I settled on the idea that my loss was due to a weak cervix. I didn't have trouble with either the conceiving or nurturing part of having a healthy baby. My trouble was in carrying the baby, and it seemed that a simple circlage could remedy the condition.

The midwives suggested waiting six weeks before resuming sexual intercourse, and the doctor recommended waiting for two normal menstrual cycles before trying to conceive again, mostly to give our minds a rest. Immediately after the loss I had wanted to get pregnant in a week. But two months after the loss I was ready to wait for many more months. My mind needed more time to heal. In six months I had gone from being pregnant and not wanting to be, to enjoying it, to losing it, and to being miserable. I had to balance out before I could handle starting over again.

I had been back at the office for a while when I realized my attitude toward work and career had changed.

The priorities of my life realigned themselves without my noticing it. I still enjoyed the excitement of a new project and the challenge of seeing all the elements come together for a deadline, but it was no longer worth my whole life to have the project succeed. Something else now meant more to me.

My interest in becoming a business tycoon would probably have diminished over the next few years anyway, but the ended pregnancy quickly brought me to some realizations about my career. I was beginning to know myself better and recognize that I didn't have the unbounded time and energy for both an all-encompassing job and a rich family life.

For me this meant not striving for the kind of job that would continually require my all, or be inflexible in its demands. There would be too many times I would not be willing to give what it took, but would instead want the freedom to invest myself elsewhere.

It wasn't a painful realization for me, but in fact encouraging for me to see how much Hugh meant to me and how much I wanted a baby. It's not that I didn't want to work hard, but I didn't want to sell out to it.

Hugh didn't comment on my new attitude. He hadn't argued with my intense desire to achieve in the business world, nor was he surprised when the desire waned. He suspected before I did that neither of us were motivated primarily by fame and fortune. I finally admitted to myself that whatever either of us did for a living, it would probably be unusual, flexible, without security, and without a job description.

Having accepted that, I found myself involved in the most interesting project yet. The architects I worked for contracted to design a New York headquarters for the Nike Corporation. The athletic wear company decided it was time for a presence in the fashion capital of the country, even though it was committed to serious athletics and the atmosphere of Beaverton, Oregon. The opening of their Manhattan office was scheduled for the fall, six months after my ended pregnancy.

The summer months were spent in preparation for the big opening, and by September I was immersed in architecture, running shoes, and publicity. Nike hired a special events coordinator in New York City to bring it all together, and my job was to assist her. I liked Peggy instantly. Older than me, with twenty years experience in the business of promotion, she showed me how she informed the press, hired caterers, planned a menu, staffed the event, and kept all aspects coordinated.

The night before the event we stuffed press packets and made last-minute calls. More than one-hundred fashion, financial, and sports writers were expected from the New York press, to mix with fashion models, corporate people, bankers, and athletes. We wanted everything to be perfect when they started arriving at 10 A.M. the next day.

I called a reporter from the *Daily News* to confirm his attendance at the event.

"Get some sleep," I said, giddy myself from the lateness of the hour.

"Are you kidding?" he replied. "We'll probably be here all night."

"Why?"

"We're tracking a hurricane. Haven't you heard 'Gloria' is due to hit New York City tomorrow morning?"

It was too late to call off our event so we proceeded as planned, but the next morning found Manhattan closed down in fear of a torrential storm that might destroy the city. It didn't matter that Gloria barely brushed past lower New York, spitting wind and rain in our direction. People were braced for the end of the world.

The Nike offices opened at 10 A.M. to a small group of reporters, models, corporate executives, and waiters. There was a lot of food, the speeches were brief, and business concluded quickly. By lunchtime, we all called it quits and went to a restaurant next door. Peggy and I looked out the window while we waited for lunch, and watched a tree bending in the wind. When the tree straightened, we knew Hurricane Gloria, an object of overpublicity, was gone.

Throughout the whole morning Peggy kept her sense of humor and never threw up her hands in defeat. I now admired her more than ever and was sorry our reason for working together was gone. I realized I didn't know much about her except that she worked alone, maintained good clients, and subcontracted other people as necessary. I didn't even know where her office was.

As I was thinking about how to stay in touch with her, she turned to me and said, "After all this, we might as well work together, don't you think?"

I was too surprised to answer, so she kept going. "Maybe you can maintain your own clients, but work with me. I have an extra desk . . ."

"Watch it," I said to myself. "This makes no sense. You're not even looking for a new job. Be wise. There's no health insurance in this deal, no guaranteed salary, no security. You need time to think."

This was not the first time in my life something looked illogical on the outside but fit on the inside. "Yes," I said out loud. "Yes, yes, yes. I'd love it."

Working with Peggy gave me something to look forward to, and I set about making the change from a big firm to a two-person office, from security to project-by-project work. Then I discovered something else to look forward to. In September, I had become pregnant. The baby was due in June.

For the second time in my life I accepted a new job and immediately found out I was pregnant. I called Dr. Balick to ask how to care for myself this time around, half expecting him to tell me not to work at all. "There's no hard evidence to show that it will help your situation to stay on your back," he said. "As a matter of fact, you'll probably do yourself a favor by working and keeping your mind off the pregnancy."

Next I called Peggy with the news, anxious to give her the option of not hiring me if she felt the pregnancy would be an obstacle to working together.

"This is fabulous news," she said without hesitation.

I didn't think she meant it. "Won't it be bothersome to some clients," I persisted, "to have a pregnant woman waddling around their special event?"

"Absolutely not. And if anyone has a problem with your being pregnant, they're not worth working for. Having a child is one of the most important things you can do. This is very exciting."

Because of her attitude I vowed to give all I could to the job, being thankful to work for someone who would also allow me to give my best to the pregnancy. Later I found out that Peggy was forty-two when she had her daughter, and counted it the best thing she had done in her life. Not only was I working for someone skilled in her field, but someone who valued motherhood. The job was right for me in more ways than I could have imagined.

My first visit to Peggy's office took me aback. The address was Olympic Tower, which sits on 5th Avenue, facing St. Patrick's Cathedral to one side and looking slightly downtown to Rockefeller Center. Aristotle Onassis built the building at the height of his wealth and power, and it still housed the offices for his domestic shipping line. Every day I walked past European boutiques and jewelry stores before turning the corner at Cartiers and pushing through the revolving doors of my new address. Security guards in red jackets quietly patrolled the lobby to the sound of a waterfall rolling down one wall into a sunken pool.

I first arrived when the building was decorated for the holidays with enormous wreaths and clusters of poinsettias. I took the elevator up to the sixth floor where a receptionist pushed a button, letting me enter the office area through tall glass doors. Models of ships as well as a wood and brass ship's wheel were on display, and I realized Peggy's space was in Onassis's own complex where his daughter, Christina, still had an office reserved for her use.

The carpeted rooms overlooking 5th Avenue were an entirely different atmosphere from the chaos of architects yelling across their boards at one another. This job also meant less running around for me and more time in the office. I was grateful for the change, and thankful to have peaceful surroundings in which to nurture my pregnancy.

In November I made an appointment with Dr. Balick to have the circlage that would hold my cervix closed. (Most circlage procedures are done between the twelfth and fourteenth weeks of pregnancy, because miscarriages are most common in the first twelve weeks, and cervical dilation doesn't normally begin until the fourteenth week.)

Dr. Balick admitted me to Roosevelt Hospital the night before the procedure. I sat on the bed in my street clothes, awkward and nervous, and thinking about my last unhappy visit to the same floor. It was Dr. Balick's humor that pulled me out.

"Nervous?" he asked, watching me crumple a Kleenex into a tiny ball. "Good. Me too. I don't know how it will turn out. I've always wanted to do one of these operations."

I began to relax just a little bit. "Incompetent cervix?" he went on. "Ah ha! Sounds serious. We've got institutions for cervixes like yours." I emitted a small chuckle.

"Good. Now someone will wheel you down to the operating room at 6 A.M. I'll be putting two stitches in your cervix, and it'll take about forty-five minutes. You'll be under general anesthesia so you won't know anything till it's over. Any questions? Good. Now, if I'm not there have one of the nurses call me; I might oversleep. You'll be there in any event."

He left me still nervous, but laughing, and I took a sleeping pill so I wouldn't lie awake thinking about every other place I'd rather be that night. I knew the risk of the circlage was minimal, but I would have to stay in the hospital for a day to make sure it didn't disturb my pregnancy by causing contractions.

The next morning Dr. B's face was the last thing I saw as the anesthesia took hold, and the first thing I saw when I came to, sick as a dog, but successfully sewn up.

"What a doctor," was all he said as I was wheeled to the recovery room, vomiting all the way. For me, the procedure was minimal compared with my reaction to the anesthesia.

The two stitches crisscrossing my cervix would remain there until they were removed several weeks before my due date. I couldn't do extreme exercise, but the circlage is generally quite successful, and I could rest assured that the stitches would not pull out from the weight of the baby.

"What happens if I start to miscarry in spite of the circlage?" I asked Dr. Balick when I could talk again.

"We cut the stitches in a hurry. Don't worry. If I'm not around, anyone can do it."

"Thanks a lot," I said. "Do I have any restrictions?"

"See this face," Dr. Balick said, squeezing his eyes shut and puffing out his cheeks. "Don't do anything that makes you look like that. Oh, and one more. You should probably avoid sexual intercourse. We're not certain if it can affect the circlage."

I noticed he used "we" to put the burden of proof on the whole medical community and not just himself. "For how long?"

"As long as it's in there."

"Hugh will love this one," I said. "It's November and the baby is due in June. You're talking abstinence."

"Use your imagination," he said, and left me to my own thoughts.

It was probably the anesthesia, but the only alternatives that came to mind were pictures from a book on erotic Indian art I had once studied to help promote an art gallery. The exotic scenes showed couples pursuing the joys of sex from impossible positions. I pictured myself hanging upside down from a swing in our bedroom, and decided abstinence might be safer.

The circlage caused only minor cramping, and in a few days I stopped thinking about it. The pregnancy progressed normally, and although I was cautious about moving too quickly or with too much strain, I felt good, and continued to work full days and rest when I got home. The only difference between me and normal pregnant women was my weekly checkup with Dr. B to make sure nothing was amiss.

My job with Peggy was a relief and a challenge. Her independence inspired me. Handling well-known clients and high-profile events, she worked spontaneously and with her whole heart, but refused to be pinned down. She preferred the uncertainty of accepting work project-by-project to the confinement of committing herself to one big corporation.

Peggy's desire for flexibility came in part from her commitment to her daughter. I had an example to follow of someone who worked hard doing what she loved, but would leave without hesitation if her daughter got sick or was in a school play. In some ways she was rooting for my pregnancy even more than I was. She knew what it was like to have a child.

At the end of January I had been with Peggy almost two months, and was a little over five months pregnant. I had heard the baby's heartbeat, felt it moving, and come to trust that the circlage was doing its job.

On January 21st I went for my checkup with Dr. Balick and he pressed on my stomach to see where the baby was growing and to measure its length. He paused too long in one place, and my heart began to beat faster.

"What is it?" I asked, sensitive to the slightest change in his expression.

"It seems the baby is growing more in the right side of your uterus than the left."

We had once talked about the possibility of my uterus showing a more pronounced malformation in the pregnant state than in its normal state. It seemed he was now finding this to be so.

"Is it okay?" I asked.

"It's okay with me, if it's okay with the baby," he said lightly, but his hands were still feeling for the baby's position.

My heart was heavy when I left, but I made an appointment for the next week so Dr. Balick could continue to monitor the baby's position. I so badly didn't want anything to be wrong.

Throughout the next morning at work my stomach was unsettled, and I had some diarrhea that kept me going to the bathroom to relieve the gas pains. I was returning to my desk for the third time when an especially sharp pain in my abdomen stopped me in my tracks and made me gasp for breath. It was followed quickly by another pain and a tightening across my whole stomach.

In one second of realization, I knew it was happening all over again. These were not gas pains but labor pains. I was in labor and I was going to lose the baby just like before. Even as I tried to digest the thought, my whole body seemed to go tight, and then my water broke all over the nice carpeted office where people were making phone calls and carrying on their business.

I wondered for a few seconds what Onassis would have thought of this situation, and then the normally subdued office erupted into activity. The horrified expressions on peoples' faces made me realize I was the only one who knew what to do. I was the only one who had been through it before.

"Please call the doctor," I said to Peggy, and calmly repeated his number when she found the line busy. "Tell him my water broke and I'll meet him at the hospital right away."

With all the determination I had, I willed Dr. Balick to be in New York City and to answer his phone. I had no room in my mind for his being gone. I needed him too badly. A voice behind me volunteered to call an ambulance, and Sharyn from the adjoining office tried to get me to sit down. By this time Peggy had Dr. Balick on the phone.

"He says to take a cab," she told me, still with a stunned expression on her face. "It'll be faster than an ambulance."

"I'm ready," I said, and headed for the door. Again, the water breaking brought momentary relief from cramps.

"Are you crazy?" said Peggy, grabbing her coat and bag and following me out of the office. "You think you're going there by yourself?" I knew what it meant for her to come with me. We had talked more than once about her fainting at the sight of blood.

Months later Peggy told me that I was the one who hailed the cab on 52nd Street and 5th Avenue and got us both in the back seat, yelling directions at the driver as we got in. In my mind I was light years beyond hysteria or sorrow. I was completely focused on getting to the hospital and having the stitches removed from my cervix before they ripped out. I was neither sad nor afraid. I was deeply, intensely furious.

At Roosevelt Hospital I propelled myself with Peggy alongside through the emergency entrance, up the elevator to the third floor, down the hall to the Ob-Gyn desk, past the nurse on duty, and into a room. I got out of my clothes, into a hospital gown, and lay down on a table to wait for Dr. Balick. Had I known how to, I would have removed my own stitches and performed the delivery. My contractions had intensified so much I knew delivery was not far away.

Peggy and the nurses did their best to comfort me, but I barely heard them. I had retreated to a small island in my mind where I waited for Dr. Balick's arrival and the end of this pregnancy. I was aware that Dr. B came in, Peggy went out, and Hugh took her place at my side. I found out later that Hugh had called our office and, upon not getting an answer, came to the hospital. He just knew.

Dr. Balick told me quickly that the stitches might already have ripped out, but he wouldn't know until he looked. I didn't care, but retreated further into my mind while being wheeled to a room where he could examine me.

"They held perfectly," he said as I was wheeled back down the hall. "I've taken them out. They were not the problem."

"What does that mean?" I asked.

"Do you always need to know everything right now?"

"Yes."

"Okay, it means an incompetent cervix was probably not the cause of this loss."

"So something else is wrong?"

"Probably, but we'll talk about it later, for God's sake, not in the middle of the hallway."

Back in my little room I faced the same lull in activity I remembered from before. Again, all we could do was wait for the delivery like a bad rerun of a situation I hated the first time. One of the nurses even recognized me and tried her best to offer words of comfort.

This time I was twenty-one weeks into the pregnancy, and there was no question of saving the fetus. For this reason, Dr. Balick offered me a painkiller as well as antinausea and antidiarrheal drugs. I had already been given a drug to speed up the labor, and they were trying to make it as easy on me as possible. I took everything they offered. It just didn't matter anymore.

The first loss had been colored by my fear and the adrenaline that accompanied it. This time was different. I knew what to expect and just had to wait for it. My mind wasn't racing, but sitting down in disgust. I could not believe this was happening again. The nurses disappeared, Dr. B left for somewhere, and Hugh again took up a vigil, sitting quietly by the window looking out at the hospital courtyard in its January bleakness.

We waited in silence. Perhaps we'd said it all the first time and didn't need to go over it again. I fingered the IV tubes and tried not to listen to the monitor keeping track of my contractions.

Dr. B reentered the room and began unloading a bag of food on the window ledge where Hugh was sitting.

"You can't have any of this" he said pointing to me. "But Hugh can. It's good, it's turkey." And he thrust a sandwich into Hugh's lap.

"You mean you're going to sit in here with us and wait?" I asked in disbelief.

"If you're asking me to lie down with you, I won't do it," he answered.

"No," I said, smiling in spite of myself. "I mean you're going to sit in here with us instead of waiting outside?" I couldn't believe he would choose to wait it out with us instead of protecting himself in some outer office.

"It so happens this is the most important place for me to be. Now shut up and let me eat. You're disturbing my dinner."

Where this radical doctor came from was a mystery to me. His unorthodox humor and willingness to be involved in my misery took me completely by surprise. He fell somewhere between a friend and a doctor. I couldn't get over both his ability to admit he didn't know something and his lightning-quick humor that made me laugh when I should have been sobbing.

He isn't tall, and his thinning hair is a continual topic of his own humor, but there isn't a sliver of diffidence in his character. "You have to have a raging ego to be a doctor," he once told me. I never asked how old he was because I didn't want to find out how close he was to my own age. I also suspected a former hippie

lay beneath the white coat, who would have worn a
ponytail had he been able.

"Are you always this funny?" I asked once when I
had to hold on to the examining table to control my
laughter.

"No. When I need to be, I'm a real bastard. You'll see
when the time comes." So far I hadn't seen it.

We made a funny trio in the bare hospital room.
Hugh seemed grateful for Dr. Balick's company as they
munched on their sandwiches. There was nothing left
for me to do but wait, so typically I began to talk.

"So what else could be wrong with me?" I asked Dr.
Balick.

"You couldn't wait till I finished eating, could you?"

"No, not if I can't eat with you."

"All right, all right," he said between bites. "Your
mother had a uterine anomaly."

"Her uterus was messed up?" I translated.

"Right. It's possible you have a similar problem. Remember the baby's positioning in the right side of your
uterus? Well, your uterus may have an anomaly that
doesn't show up when you're not pregnant, but becomes
pronounced during pregnancy, dividing it into two horns
at the top. The baby is decidedly sitting in the right
half of the uterus."

"Can it be fixed?" I asked, already accepting the idea
of a malformed uterus.

"There is surgery that can fix a bicornuate uterus,
joining the two horns at the top, if it is indeed your
problem. Your mother had a different problem, which

they also corrected with surgery. She had a piece of tissue or septum growing down into her uterus that can also prevent a fetus from growing to full size. We need to take a closer look at you and see what conditions are present."

"Later?"

"Well, I'm not going to do it now. We have another problem right now."

He didn't need to remind me; my contractions were coming harder and faster, and I knew we didn't have long. It must have been obvious because Hugh was already on his feet, his hand in mine, ready for the last effort.

Dr. Balick was on his feet too, pulling on gloves and readying himself for the delivery.

"Do you have a girlfriend, Dr. B?" I asked suddenly, trying desperately to divert his attention and postpone what I knew was coming.

"You are something else," he said shaking his head. "Could it be it's none of your business?"

I didn't answer.

"Okay," he said, relenting. "I do. Are you satisfied?"

"Yes," I said meekly, knowing there was no more postponing.

My second experience with delivery was slightly easier than the first time. I knew what I faced and wasn't as scared. Hugh and I prewarned Dr. Balick that we didn't want to see or handle the baby, and didn't want an autopsy unless he felt it was necessary. There would be no difficult decisions on the spot. We had already made them.

At 4:15 P.M., six hours after my water broke, I delivered a tiny boy, dead at birth, but seemingly perfectly formed. I was less alert this time, having taken every drug I could, and only wanting to get out of there as fast as possible.

My calm must have unsettled Dr. Balick, who stayed in the room with us after I was cleaned up and resting on a fresh sheets.

"Look," he said suddenly earnest. "It's okay if you want to cry, or scream at me, or hit the bed. You don't have to be a saint about this. It's a miserable situation and you don't have to be stoic. You're going to need to deal with it sometime. The first jerk who says something stupid to you, you have my permission to curse him out. Or send him to me. As long as he's small and unarmed, of course."

By this time his hand was around mine, and I held on for all I was worth. "I want a baby," I managed to say. "I don't want to scream at you because I need you around to help me get one."

"I'll be here," he answered, and I believed him. "Meanwhile you've got to take care of yourself. Hugh?" he motioned for Hugh to come over. "Call me when you two feel ready to leave the hospital, and I'll discharge you." He transferred my hand to Hugh's, and left the room.

Hugh and I went home that night, and I settled back on my couch, stunned, quiet, and not believing what I just went through. We didn't immediately tell our families of this second loss. It was my parents' wedding anniversary and I didn't want to ruin it.

The aftermath of this second loss resembled the first one, but without the drama. My mind wasn't spinning, or reeling, or asking "why?" The crisis didn't stimulate me as it did the first time. I was simply numb.

For several days I sat on the couch under a quilt with my legs stretched out in front of me. I had a lot more pain this time, and I didn't want to move. The first time I had expelled the afterbirth with no problem. This time Dr. Balick had to wrestle it out of me. I was sore, cramping and bleeding, and mad, mad, mad. With resignation, I found the oversized shirt my mother gave me the year before, and waited for my milk to come in. There would be no surprises this time.

When people called to ask how I was, I didn't know what to say. How am I supposed to be? I wondered. I'm surprised I'm still living. I didn't think I could make it if this ever happened to me again, and now it's happened for the second time in ten months. How am I? I don't know. I don't know anything anymore. Nothing makes sense. I'm off-balance, uncertain, raw, fragile, and I hate this situation.

The more I thought about it, the more I realized I had been robbed. I remembered the feeling when our apartment was broken into and I came home to find my clothing strewn around the bedroom, and all my jewelry gone. I felt the same way now, only worse. I was being robbed of my joy, my dreams, and my life as a mother. I didn't want sympathy, and I didn't want flowers, I wanted to be someone else in a different country. I didn't know what I wanted. Furious with my body, I was also scared of whatever it was doing to me.

My natural resiliency helped me get over the first loss and keep going, but I had run out of it. Helplessly I pulled the quilt tighter around me. How in the world would I make it through this one? My back was to the wall and I could see no way to turn.

Mercifully, my brain turned into ice and I felt nothing. I didn't care if Hugh went to work and left me. I didn't care if people came to visit. I half expected most of my friends to be angry with me for losing a second time and for demanding more sympathy than they had to give. I didn't even care when my milk came in, but put on a tight bra and refused to pay any attention to my breasts whatsoever.

For many hours I sat on the couch with the quilt up to my chin, watching the January days turn dark by 4 P.M. I was waiting for something, but I didn't know what. Maybe spring would come and thaw the ice, and I would be able to feel again.

7 . The Skylight

Meggan's voice on the phone was a welcome sound. Life for her is black and white, not tinged with hundreds of nuances and possible meanings. If you're sick, you need to get better; if you're unhappy, you need to take a break; if you just lost a pregnancy for the second time, you need to get out of New York City for the weekend and change your perspective.

In her matter-of-fact approach she presented a plan. "Now you may be grumpy, miserable, and hard to get along with, but you might as well come with us to my parents' house for the weekend and be grumpy there. It will just be the four of us and we can rent movies and look at Long Island Sound. What do you think?"

It sounded good to me. When Hugh and I moved to Manhattan, Meggan and her husband Konrad walked us through much of the initial confusion of the city. They understood rent controlled apartments, alternate-side-of-the-street parking, and how to tip taxi drivers.

Later on they helped us haul our furniture to a new apartment on the Upper West Side, met us for movies, and recommended restaurants for us to try. I continued to value Meggan's interpretation of events when I faced job problems, confidence slumps, and salary negotiations.

Meggan became a commercial real estate appraiser when it was essentially a man's field, was hired by an international bank, and traveled frequently on business, all the while stating that she's really lazy at heart and would rather read all day and drink soda on the couch. Her calm exterior hides a wit so quick she often has to apologize for it. In a complex situation she's quick to identify the elements and package them in one sentence. More important, she knows how to be a great friend.

We accepted the invitation to her parents' home about twenty miles outside the city. It's a modern house with a lawn sloping down to an inlet of Long Island Sound, and we had it to ourselves for two days. We drove up on Saturday in Konrad's faithful Mustang and immediately felt the absence of Manhattan's fever pitch.

Stepping out of the car we collided with the smell of salt water and seaweed, and could hear gulls calling to each other from the boat docks. I pulled my coat tightly around me and walked around to the back terrace. The cold ocean air made my heart beat faster, and even the desolate puddles of low tide looked beautiful in the stark morning light.

At first the pregnancy loss hung over us and made us awkward where we'd never had trouble talking before. Meggan, always sensitive to peoples' moods, was painfully aware of mine. She knew, and was later proved right, that she would conceive easily and have a text-book pregnancy. This made it harder for her to watch my failed attempts. Even Konrad was quiet, hesitant to unleash his normal humor lest it be inappropriate this time.

I tried to relieve the atmosphere by assuring them I was all right. Gradually we relaxed and organized the welcome task of buying food and drink, and deciding what to do with our time off. As the day progressed we spread ourselves around the house, thankful for the space and the view and the silent phone. Meggan and I picked up our ongoing conversation about life in our thirties and wondering when we'd ever feel like adults.

I thought of the weekend as a time to get away not only physically but mentally. I was tired of the weight of sickness, death, and loss. If it were possible to dis-tract or numb my mind for the two days, I wanted to try. I was already taking codeine pills to dull the cramp-ing in my stomach. I thought getting drunk might dull my mind.

The men left in the late afternoon and returned with rented videos, sandwiches, and six-packs of beer. With deliberation I began to drink, knowing I was among forgiving company. The worst I could do was say some-thing stupid and fall off the couch.

I looked forward to my mind straying off into the wilderness, and I drank along with the movies we watched. *Chariots of Fire* was good for two beers, *Amadeus* for two more. We took a break for sandwiches and another beer for me. As we started into Woody Allen, my cramps were gone but my thoughts marched on with relentless clarity.

Partway into *Annie Hall* I decided sleep was the only way out. Whatever part of me came from Ireland and could sit for long hours in pubs without getting drunk, moved to the fore. The more I drank the less effect it seemed to have.

Meggan had arranged for Hugh and me to stay in an upstairs room with a skylight, sliding doors onto a terrace, a private bathroom, and an enormous bed that could sleep a small neighborhood. I pulled my body to a standing position and excused myself from the group. Hugh glanced up to check if I was all right, and I assured everyone I was truly tired and climbed upstairs, expecting the alcohol to put me right to sleep.

Lying down I quickly realized how far from sleep I was. Not only that, my thoughts were clear. If the alcohol did anything, it added poignancy to the situation. A strong wind I hadn't noticed before blew rain across the skylight. Lying in the darkness, I could hear bursts of laughter from the group below. I was warm, protected, surrounded by loving friends, and utterly alone with my problem. How unfair.

As soon as I focused on "unfair," a wealth of evidence sprang to mind to support the thought. One pregnancy loss could be a case of random percentages I reasoned, but two was an indicator of something drastically wrong. I felt like a boxer who had been knocked out by an unseen opponent. Struggling to my feet, I looked up briefly only to find myself knocked out a

second time by a blow from behind. The rules of this
match had gone haywire, and I no longer knew how to
compete.

"You've been sucker punched," said a slippery little
voice in my mind. "And victimized."

"Think of it," the voice went on, gaining momentum. "You're lying there like a lonely cow with a swollen
udder and no one to give milk to."

My mind, which had been ice cold the week before,
was beginning to thaw and drip one negative thought
after another. "Oh, your body works okay, except you
can't carry babies. You're built like women down through
the ages, but you can't do the one thing women were
designed to do by nature, give birth to a child.

"Think of it, the one thing you should be able to do
easily and you can't do it. Why you, anyway? What have
you done to bring this on yourself? Your body wants to
have a baby; gives you the opportunity once a month to
fulfill itself, but you can't do it.

"That's right, I said fulfill yourself. Face it. You think
you're a success because you work in a fancy office and
people pay you do to it. But that's not enough is it?
What you really need is to have a baby and raise a child.
That's what your body is designed to do, but you never
will."

Peversely, I allowed these thoughts to run loose,
followed by the self-pity and pessimism I had held at
bay for so long. I knew I was being melodramatic, but
then the accusations took on a life of their own and the
darkness around me filled with recrimination.

"What's more, you gained weight with the first loss and never took it off. Now you're just going to get fatter and fatter because you have no incentive to lose it. To add insult to injury, you could breast feed triplets, but you'll never have a baby to nurse.

"Of course, you could adopt. But you know the stories you've heard. It will take forever and you don't have the money, and you'll end up adopting a child from a foster home who had drug addicted parents. Could you handle that? Poor, poor you."

By this time I felt so sorry for myself tears were streaming down my cheeks and rolling into my ears. One sob followed another and I cried with all the despair of two years of disappointments and a long road ahead. I cried for what might have been, what wasn't, and what might never be.

My mind filled with hopelessness in a way I'd never experienced before, and I couldn't pull it back with my customary good humor. I wondered if I were going insane thinking about shattered dreams and how hard life is, and getting older, getting sick, and dying. I hadn't really faced death, and it threw me.

Alone in the big bedroom with the sound of waves knocking against the dock outside, I faced more than depression and sorrow, I faced my life gone awry, and life inside me that couldn't get started, and the futility and brevity of my time on earth, and with it all came some of the hollowest fear I'd ever felt.

Years earlier, when I was eighteen, I shared a room with my grandmother on a family vacation. We were on the south coast of England in an ancient town, staying in a tiny old house with uneven stairs and dormer windows.

I awoke in the middle of the night to the sound of waves outside and the sound of my grandmother talking in the next bed. Something in the tone of her voice kept me from speaking or even moving. I thought she was praying, but realized she was reciting from the Psalms in a quiet, steady voice:

"O magnify the Lord with me, and let us exalt his name together. I sought the Lord, and he heard me, and delivered me from all my fears. They looked unto him, and were lightened: and their faces were not ashamed."

I knew she was sick though she would never talk about it, and I knew she was lying awake fighting things I didn't understand yet. Now, I understood a little better. I wasn't the first one to wrestle with fear and need my understanding lightened in the night hours.

By this time, sobbing had given me a headache, and had not done me any good. As my tears quieted into hiccoughs, I was still alone and still didn't have a baby.

"Oh God," I whispered into the silence, "deliver me from all my fears. If I don't change my thinking I might as well die. Somewhere there's a way out of this, and I need to see it before I sink under my own despair."

I looked up through the skylight. The rain had stopped and I could see an expanse of night sky with stars flickering very far away. I remembered those stars from Montana. They hadn't changed but I had been living where I couldn't see them. As I looked, their number seemed to increase, and I slowly let myself acknowledge the enormity of what displayed itself above me. Its order and logic stretched out forever on either side of my short little life. The thought awed and thrilled me at the same time.

What kind of power allows the universe to work? The vastness of the enterprise makes a nine-month pregnancy seem like child's play. If a divine authority keeps billions of heavenly bodies moving precisely so they show up at the right place at the right time, then surely I could draw upon that power to help my earthly body deliver a baby on schedule.

At one time I understood how to trust God no matter what the circumstances looked like, but lately the circumstances were all I could see. In my heart I knew that what I wanted was available to me. One way or another there would be a baby in my life.

"We're going to do it, God," I said aloud. "I'm going to have a baby. Surely, if you care about the path of a planet, you care about my life."

I heard my own words and in a tiny banner of trust unfurled in the back of my mind. There's an inexplicable peace that comes from acknowledging a power larger than yourself. I had let the failed pregnancies rob me of that peace, and would need to reestablish it in my heart before I tried again to have a baby.

I thought of Sara, Abraham's wife, who finally accepted God's grace and had a son when she was ninety-nine years old.

"And God," I added, "I'd like to have a baby before I'm ninety-nine." The very thought made me tired.

"Maybe I'll just close my eyes for a while, and think about this again in the morning." I gave a halfhearted hiccough and turned the pillow, feeling for a dry spot. With my mind finally emptied, I fell asleep.

Back in New York City, waiting for March to give up and let spring arrive, I kept remembering that night in the big bed with the skylight above me, and the relief in focusing on something bigger and more powerful than myself. Even thought it didn't prevent me from periodically falling into the same mental ruts, I knew more what I was up against, and I knew where relief lay.

Of the many elements in my quest to have a baby—my husband, the medical world, my job, and even my body—almost none of them was solely under my power. The only thing I had power to control was my mind. If I didn't learn to control my thoughts, they would run away with me on a path of self-pity and despair that was difficult to reverse.

I had heard an expression years before that now took on new meaning: "The greatest cargoes of life come in over quiet seas." My need for peace of mind outstripped my need for a baby. A flag of trust waved feebly somewhere in my heart. I had to learn which thoughts and activities allowed it to keep flying, and which ones ripped it down. Over the next months I worked harder on my mind than on my body. That was where the real battle raged.

8 . Things That Help

I was now thirty-one years old and had lost two pregnancies in two years. My formerly cheerful demeanor was showing some scars, and I no longer took for granted my good health, future motherhood, or stories with happy endings. Having a baby was taking on enormous proportions for me the more I thought about it.

The two losses left me in a constant mental battle. My initial struggle was in managing my grieving heart concerning all that had happened. After a period of time, the new struggle was in urging my heart to remain peaceful about the future.

Over time, I learned some things to do that helped me control my emotions when grief, despair, or anxiety threatened at the door. The more I talked with women in similar circumstances, the more I realized there were basic ways of dealing with pregnancy loss that we all relied on, and were eager to share with others.

About the heaviness of grief, it is the natural, healthy reaction to loss. Mercifully, it isn't constant but comes in waves, probably because the finality of death is so shocking it can't be taken in all at once, but has to be absorbed little by little.

I have heard that when we lose a loved one, it can take a full year before the grief begins to lessen because we need to live through one of each holiday, season, and special occasion without the person before we start to grasp his or her absence. There is a natural lessening of grief over time, and eventually we give up the deep sorrow and move on. We are not built to carry the heartache indefinitely.

In my ended pregnancies I wasn't mourning the loss of someone I knew, but the loss of my expectations and dreams. I did not wonder what the babies would have been like had they lived, because they did not live. For me it was that simple. Instead, I mourned the absence of something I knew was my right to have, that I had invested in, and desperately wanted.

I think an ended pregnancy carries a different kind of sorrow for women who already have children than for those who don't. A mother understands more deeply the potential of what is lost. On the other hand, someone like me, who was still childless, wrestles with that hollow fear that maybe she'll never be able to give birth to a healthy baby.

I found that after each of my losses the initial grief was intense and frequent. Sorrow loomed suddenly like an eclipse of the sun, only to leave as quickly as it came. During those difficult moments I often picked up my diary and wrote down what I was thinking. Writing helped me clarify what I was going through, and then leave it behind on the pages of the journal.

Another habit I developed was to find Hugh and talk with him. Many times I called him at work and said simply, "Hi, this is me going through a hard time." He'd tell me he understood, and the load would be lightened.

Sometimes, if I were alone, I would allow myself to cry and talk out loud. "Okay," I'd say to myself. "You feel pretty bad right now. Life sure seems grim. Your heart hurts. This isn't an easy moment. But something good can come out of it. You're going to have increased compassion after all this. Maybe you can eventually help someone else going through the same thing. Oh, go ahead and cry, you've got to let it out somehow."

After several weeks, I passed from intense sorrow, to spurts of sadness, to periodic feelings of unhappiness. Many times I thought I was completely over the grief when it would resurface unexpectedly to let me know it wasn't all gone. It didn't always follow a reminder of pregnancy, but often seemed unrelated.

One summer morning I took a bus to work and settled toward the back in a stream of air conditioning. As usual I observed the other riders and thought about the strange clustering of characters in New York City. An elderly man slowly climbed into the bus and shuffled down the aisle. He had dressed with care as if to ward off creeping age and loneliness, and with difficulty lowered himself into a seat and sat with his hands trembling slightly in his lap.

Suddenly my heart filled with sorrow and my eyes clouded with tears I couldn't stop. I bent my head to avoid the gaze of the passengers opposite me and found to my dismay more and more tears falling onto my lap. My sadness was all out of proportion to the man's situation, and I wondered if I were losing my sanity. If his weakness bothered me, what would I do when I got on the street and saw the homeless sleeping on benches or beggars with their paper cups?

It took me several minutes to realize the tears came from deep within and had nothing to do with the old man. It was just a wave of heartache triggered by a sad scene. When I recognized what was happening, the heaviness subsided and I continued the ride in control of myself. After that I realized when I laughed to the point of tears, or overreacted to a scene in a movie, I was merely releasing a remnant of inner sorrow that had worked its way to the surface.

When the initial grief from my losses lightened, I faced the new fight of whether to get pregnant again and, if I did, how to make it through without anxiety. I discovered two opposing cycles in my mind, one where I believed everything would turn out all right, and the other where I feared everything would continue to go wrong and bring me years of pain. I had to discover what set me off in either direction, and how to care for my thoughts to keep me on the positive cycle.

I did not fully confront the possibility of never having a child because I believed my body would eventually carry a healthy baby, even if it meant more failures in the process. In the back of mind I held onto adoption as the natural recourse if we came to a point where I couldn't bear to try again. At the time, however, I wanted to continue trying to have our own child, even though my expectations could bounce from victory to defeat and back again in a matter of minutes.

In some instances talking helped ease my confusion and let me see where I was and where I was headed. If I could say to someone, "Well, I lost two pregnancies, but there may be a problem in my uterus that can be fixed," I reinforced for myself that it was indeed possible for me to have a child; it would only be a matter of time.

On the other hand, if I talked about it too much, the negatives of the situation overwhelmed me and I would realize how little physical evidence there was for my having a baby. Too much talk plunged me into pessimism again.

Although I drew comfort from talking with women in similar situations, I had to be careful which direction the conversations took. Always, I was relieved to discover I wasn't alone in my battle. However, other women could introduce fears I had never even considered, and then I'd have to deal with a whole new set.

One well-meaning friend showed me an issue of a newsletter written especially for DES daughters. I began to read the personal accounts of women trying to conceive, and quickly realized how much could go wrong with me I had never known about. Instead of being comforted, I had to fight not to worry about each of their problems becoming my own.

Another friend, however, sent me an Ob/Gyn journal that chronicled the results of women trying to have a baby after multiple miscarriages due to uterine anomalies. The conclusion drawn was that, after surgery, and sometimes with no surgical intervention, most went on to have a healthy pregnancy and full-term delivery. I kept that journal on my desk within reach for difficult moments.

After I learned to identify which situations set me off on a negative path, I either avoided them or fortified my mind. At one point when I was having a particularly difficult time emotionally, I was invited to a baby shower for a friend having her fifth child. The prospect of focusing for two hours on babies and baby gifts overwhelmed me. I declined the invitation, explaining to the hostess of the shower why I could not attend and asking her to extend my apologies wherever necessary.

I categorically avoided any magazine or newspaper article describing a situation such as "Woman with cancer wins lawsuit against DES drug manufacturer." The headline alone was hard for me to handle; the article itself would not contribute to my state of mind.

On the other hand, I could not avoid every baby on Broadway or every pregnant woman in New York. Neither could I avoid the fact that most of my married friends were having babies with no trouble. In those cases, I prepared my mind to fight.

First I tried to separate my life from everyone else's and refused to compare myself to other women. If other women were having three children by the time they were thirty, that was fine, but it wasn't my life. If my friends became pregnant in one try and carried to full term with no problems, fine, but that wasn't the way it was for me. They had areas of difficulty also, maybe it just wasn't in childbirth. I could be thankful for all the areas of my life that were prospering, and patiently wait for this area to fall in line.

Hugh uses an expression I've adopted for my own. He often speaks of not "going down a road" in his mind. He means not allowing himself to take a certain train of thought if there is no profit in it. For instance there is no profit in dwelling on what life would be like had I married a different person, or tried to get pregnant when I was twenty instead of thirty, or lived in the country instead of the city.

When I learned how my thoughts strained to go down roads leading to nowhere, I stopped them early before they could pick up momentum and take on a life of their own. For instance, when I talked to one of my former roommates on the phone, I learned she had become pregnant by accident, and was enjoying a healthy pregnancy in spite of not really wanting a baby at this time. This was a sure trigger for my thinking how unfair life is, and why couldn't I carry a baby to term, and why do things go right for her and not for me when she doesn't even want a baby?

After the phone call, depression knocked at the door, so I addressed it head on: "I do not care what happens to other women, I have my own life to live. I'm sick of being jealous about other peoples' babies, and will not allow it anymore." Then I quickly found something else to get into before my thoughts coaxed me back down that road.

When I took the time to identify what set me off and counteracted it, I avoided the cloud of abstract unhappiness that so easily descended around me. Eventually I didn't have to fight so hard. Certain roads in my mind were closed, and I no longer tried to go down them.

At one point after my second loss, I was referred to a counselor forming a support group for women with either high-risk pregnancies or a history of pregnancy loss. I carefully considered whether or not to join, and finally decided against it.

In my day-to-day life I met many women in my situation and had no lack of conversation and companionship on the subject. I enjoyed the flexibility of calling someone when I needed to, and the informality of our talks. I did not seek more contact in this area. Also, I felt that listening to a full range of pregnancy problems might do me more harm than good.

Many women with no way to put their experience in perspective find the help they need in a support group. Additionally they find an outlet for talking that they may not have in their day-to-day life. The group I was invited to join cost more money than I was willing to spend. Ideally these groups should be free, staffed by volunteers who want to help others because of successfully handling the problem in their own lives. Increasingly, they are available in many communities and can be found through hospital contacts.

The day I met Jodie was the day I found a built-in support group in my own neighborhood, and realized the value of having one person to talk to about pregnancy. Flamboyant and funny, Jodie was designing a high-powered Valentine's Day gift basket when I first encountered her. Our office was promoting the restaurant Jodie worked for, and therefore Peggy and I had to fully experience one of these baskets. We found each ribbon, cupid, and carefully wrapped piece of Swiss chocolate anchored lovingly in a sea of red tissue paper and satin fabric.

Jodie, the artist, has a cloud of wavy dark hair, a flawless complexion, a voluptuous figure, and a tiny diamond in one nostril. In comparison, I look like a banker. Within minutes of meeting, however, we discovered we lived one block from each other and both had lost pregnancies. Both of us were questionable or high-risk patients, and wanted desperately to have babies.

Before long Jodie and I established a relationship in which we could discuss our problems and solutions, expectations, questions, and general conclusions on the subject of pregnancy. Jodie thought about it even more than I did, and was therefore ready at any moment to address the topic. She never grew tired of the details, and I didn't need to be concerned about boring her or scaring her with the things on my mind.

Both at work and with my acquaintances I soon stopped discussing my ended pregnancies and my thoughts for the future. With Jodie, however, I always found a listening ear and an understanding heart. Having one person to talk to who was positive, funny, and going through the same things at the same time filled a great need in my life, and left me free to focus on other matters in my other relationships.

Jodie and I discovered for ourselves some of the common ways women have handled the frustration of losing pregnancies. For instance, finding the opportunity to talk with someone in the same situation who doesn't mind a phone call for support when times are tough, and who will let you talk out the difficult decisions.

We also found great comfort in older people who had lived through a few hard times of their own. Our parents and grandparents generation can offer great wisdom and perspective on handling death and difficult times. They've learned the sun still comes up in the morning even when it seems the world has ended. Sitting for a while with a woman in her seventies or eighties who has weathered a few storms is a good way to put troubles in perspective.

In addition to writing down my thoughts, I found comfort in reading books about any subject except pregnancy. A friend gave me essays by E. B. White, some of which contained reflections on World War II, and I thought how trifling were my own conflicts in comparison. I read adventures, westerns, and novels covering subjects bigger than my life. They all helped divert my mind from my own condition and show me that pregnancy was not the only thing happening in the world.

In keeping with my ongoing desire to see what lies behind the physical world we live in, I sought spiritual understanding concerning my own struggle to have a baby. I found myself in good company, discovering that an ended pregnancy is enough to send the most pragmatic women looking for spiritual explanations.

Pregnancy loss is enough of a strain physically and emotionally, when, in addition, you have to confront your beliefs about life and death, and chance and fate. Instead of joyfully anticipating a birth, you face untimely death, questions about when life really begins, what happens after death, and all manner of far-reaching concepts that don't ordinarily preoccupy your thinking.

By the time I started my third pregnancy I had encountered an array of beliefs that people relied on when the medical world had been exhausted. One acquaintance of mine had a child and was unsuccessfully trying for another. "I think it's all spiritual," she confessed one day when we were walking through Central Park. "I believe spirits of babies hang around until they're ready to come into the world, and then they arrive. They come in their own timing and to the woman they choose. I'm just waiting for the one who's chosen me."

Another woman also newly pregnant, invited me over for tea one Saturday afternoon. After we talked for a while, she pulled something out of her pocket and put it on the table, still covered by her hand. "Now you may not believe in this," she said somberly. "But I want you to have it. It can't hurt if you just carry it around through the pregnancy."

She pushed her hand across the table and uncovered a small, whitish rock. "It's a healing crystal," she said.

"Now don't think I'm crazy, but I got one for both of us because they might work."

Many of my acquaintances, searching for why pregnancies fail, finally resigned themselves to the hands of fate: "I guess it just wasn't meant to be. If it's meant to be, it'll happen."

Personally I was most at home with the Biblical viewpoint of life, which describes not a capricious God, but one who is loving, and works according to laws and principles easily understood. I knew my desire to have a baby was not contradictory, but rather in harmony with the entire design of the universe. I needed to put aside the anxieties I had allowed to fill my mind, and trust that it was available for me one way or another to have a child in my life.

I remembered an Old Testament psalm that says to delight yourself in the Lord and he will give you the desires of your heart. I knew it was speaking to me. I needed to extricate myself for a while from the mountain of medical information piling up in my life and concentrate on higher things.

I began looking through the Bible for keys to keeping my peace of mind and seeing the desire of my heart come to pass. I found the record in the Old Testament of Hannah, a woman happily married but unable to have children. Over the years her sorrow increased until she could barely eat for the ache of not having a baby.

On a feast day, Hannah went alone to the temple to pray. Kneeling down, she began to pour out her heart to God about the years of trying, the failure, and the anguish that would not be comforted even by a loving husband. She wept, laying her whole life before God with its bitterness and abundance of grief. And she asked for His help.

Her tears dried and, her heart finally at peace, she went on to have a son nine months later, and in the following years three more sons and two daughters.

I read and reread every account of women who were barren but went on to have children long before the days of laparoscopies, sonograms, in-vitro fertilization, hormone therapy, and circlages. I was thankful for the medical help available to me, but I needed to set a few things straight in my own heart about what I really wanted to rely on in this situation.

One of the greatest laws interwoven throughout the Bible is the law of believing. Basically what one is convinced of, either positively or negatively, happens. To a great extent the information we feed our minds is what we end up believing and seeing come to pass in our lives.

Focusing on an object or circumstance, and being convinced from the heart that it will happen, begins to open doors so that it will happen. If a person can quiet down her thoughts, become clear on what she wants to see happen, and be concerned enough to keep the picture in her mind for more than a week, she's well on the road to getting it.

This law, similar to gravity, is difficult to argue with, and there's nothing religious about it. It works whether a person believes in God or not. Neither is this a new discovery, or a complicated one, or one that many people take the time to analyze. It simply works. It works in business, athletics, personal relationships, and health. But if you understand it spiritually, it works better. Because if you're willing to admit there's power and wisdom greater than your own, the results are no longer limited to your own abilities.

The difficulty for most is in being able to keep the mind focused for more than thirty seconds on any one thing, and in having the meekness to accept spiritual help. I learned that, for me, having a baby was not automatic, but rather would require much effort on my part, physically, mentally, and spiritually.

The pregnancy losses brought me face to face with the limits of my own ability. I needed God's help, and knew praying and believing was the place to start. Years earlier I hadn't been disappointed when I trusted God to meet my needs. I had to recapture that trust.

In our marriage, Hugh and I arrived at the point where we wanted to keep trying to have a baby whether it meant more medical procedures, the possibility of another loss, the possibility of a long time, or the possibility of adoption. After that, it was my job to keep my heart calm, looking for the open doors to help me have a child, and not allowing myself to get consumed with worry or obsessed over the idea.

I could continue to look for the next step that was right for my situation, expecting something to be there. Meanwhile I could enjoy the things going right in our lives while I waited for the arrival of a baby somehow, from somewhere.

9 . Pregnant Again

I don't know when a woman who has lost a pregnancy is finally ready to try again. It's sometime after the grief subsides, after the reminders of pregnancy stop hurting so much, and after the body works normally again. In a phone call with Caroline Rawlins, the doctor I turned to after my first loss, she told me in her most blunt manner, "There's no other way to have a baby than to try again. If you don't, you won't, so get going."

She went on to say that sometimes she meets husbands who tell her, "I don't want my wife to try again because I can't stand to see her hurt if it fails." She sits the husband down and tells him, "If you really want to see your wife hurt, try to protect her from having another loss. In the long run, trying again is the only way to get over it."

In my case, before we tried again there were more medical procedures to be done. At this point I recognized the conservative nature of the medical profession in the area of miscarriage. Dr. Balick told me that for a long time doctors did not even start serious investigations until a patient had three first-trimester losses. I was the victim of "repeated second-trimester spontaneous abortions," and further investigation was definitely warranted.

My second loss proved that an incompetent cervix was not the only problem I had. Because of the way the recent pregnancy grew in only the right side of my uterus, the next thing to look for was a structural problem in the uterus itself. Even though they thought my uterus was not bicornuate, it had responded during pregnancy as if it were.

In the earlier examination, called a hysterosalpingogram, they could see a subtle indentation at the top of the uterus that did not warrant surgery. But perhaps it was the cause of my uterus growing unevenly during my second pregnancy.

Now, Dr. Balick recommended further investigation via a procedure called a laparoscopy. A telescopic device would pass into an incision near my navel, through which the doctor could view the outside of the uterus. In my case they wanted to see if the top of my uterus separated into two horns like the top of a heart (a bicornuate uterus), or if the "dip" was only on the inside.

If my uterus were indeed bicornuate, they would end the laparoscopy right there. Hugh and I would then discuss with the doctors further surgery that might rejoin the two "horns" to give the uterus a smooth, rounded top.

If the laparoscopy showed no abnormality on the outside of the uterus, then, while I was still under anaesthesia, the doctor would go on to perform a hysteroscopy. In this procedure, a hysteroscope passes into the uterus through the vagina, through which the doctor can perform microsurgery on the uterine wall. The director of Obstetrics and Gynecology at St. Lukes-Roosevelt Hospital was Dr. Robert Neuwirth, and at the time was one of the few doctors in the country experienced in using the hysteroscope for microsurgery. Dr. Balick would ask him about my case.

It sounded complicated, but I understood the principle. Armed with sketches of hearts and circles and arrows, I went home to Hugh and we saw no reason not to give it a try. To me, anything we did was preferable to just getting pregnant again and wishing the same things wouldn't go wrong. At least if there were a visible problem, they could probably fix it.

In May, about four months after the second loss, I went into the hospital for surgery. For someone who had never been in a hospital until age thirty-one, I was making up for lost time. Everything by now was familiar to me: the hallway, shower, smells, uncomfortable green chairs; even my roommate seemed like an old acquaintance.

As before, I was in the maternity ward in a semiprivate room. I had finally gone on an insurance plan that would cover the operation as well as a future pregnancy. It would not, however, cover a private room and, in keeping with the primary nature of the ward, my roommate had a new baby.

Over a four-year span of visiting Roosevelt Hospital
for various emergencies and procedures, I had an array
of roommates. After my pregnancy losses the doctors
made sure I wasn't in a room with a new mother, but
during my operations many of my roommates had new
babies. A shy, young Oriental girl was by far the quiet-
est, and her baby equally serene. I grew to appreciate
her silent pack of relatives after my later experiences.

This time especially, my room was a carnival. I shared
it with a German woman who had fallen in love with a
Spanish television newscaster, and had his baby the day
before I arrived. Already strewn with flowers, balloons,
bottles of champagne, mounds of cookies and pink tissue paper, the room continued to fill with friends and
relatives, both Spanish and German, long into the
night. Most of the relatives wanted to be as close as
possible, and in the bed if available, with the new
mother. I actually looked forward to the anesthesia to
give me rest.

The night before the operation Dr. Neuwirth came
by for a preop visit. We had not met before, although I
had checked up on his reputation through a friend of
mine who worked in the hospital system. Her evalua-
tion came back: quiet, but highly experienced.

Quiet was an understatement. An older man with
steel gray hair, Dr. Neuwirth had a reserved air that left
me dumb. I had grown so accustomed to bantering with
Dr. Balick that I had forgotten how intimidating some
medical figures can be. Dr. Neuwirth had me sign some

papers, and asked if I had any questions. My comments died on my lips, so we shook hands and said good night.

In the morning I showered and waited. How strange to sit on a hospital bed, perfectly healthy, waiting to be wheeled away to an operation. My roommate was already on the phone to Germany, and there was no one else to talk to.

I sat cross-legged on the bed and thought about the time some of us drove across MacDonald Pass outside of Helena, Montana, at midnight in a snowstorm. At the absolute peak of the mountain, in a driving wind, we got a flat tire. I remember crouching behind a snowdrift knowing by morning we would either be frozen statues by the side of the road, or sitting at breakfast telling the story of how we got off the mountain.

That's how I felt as the anesthesia took hold. By lunchtime I would either be a woman with a complicated uterus that looked like a heart and needed surgery, or everything would be taken care of, and I'd be free to get pregnant again.

My doctor, the silver phantom, had been here and gone by the time I was conscious enough to register my surroundings. The mood around me seemed victorious. Dr. Balick was by my bed waiting to tell me that Dr. Neuwirth found my uterus to be normal from the outside, and had then gone inside to remove a small piece of tissue. Hugh was upstairs waiting for me, and I could believe that everything had gone as well as could be desired. Again, sick as a dog from the drugs, I went for three days before the anesthesia seemed gone from my body. Other than that, I was fine.

Technically the procedure was called a "hysteroscopic resection of uterine septum and laparoscopy." In order to promote the healing of my uterus, Dr. Neuwirth prescribed hormones for me to take for six weeks. After that I was to wait a few months before trying to get pregnant, giving my uterus further time to heal. It meant that Hugh and I could start trying again in September.

Summer in New York City is legendary for miserable humidity that makes tempers fly at the slightest provocation. Heat presses down among the tall buildings causing the sidewalks to steam, and the smell of too many people in damp clothing fills the lobbies and elevators. As many people as possible leave the city for as long as they can, and many seem to have an unspoken agreement that on Friday afternoons work ends early.

During the summer following my second loss I still worked for Peggy, but she had disappeared to Ireland for a month. Business was slow because many of our clients had gone to equally far-off places. Hugh and I were still in the city, but eagerly accepted invitations to visit friends who lived in cool, neighboring states, or who had access to a place to swim.

After many, many months of keeping records of my period, counting days, tracking ovulation, using birth control or not using it, alternately hoping to be pregnant or not pregnant, I felt curiously indifferent to what happened. I believed my next pregnancy had a good opportunity to succeed, and I was ready to let it happen in its own time.

It was fun in the beginning of August when Hugh and I looked at each other and simultaneously said, "Oh, what the hell." Contrary to the deliberate, calculated steps we had taken for so long, we stopped using birth control, stopped counting, and figured I would get pregnant eventually and meanwhile take life one day at a time.

It wasn't even a month before I started to suspect it had already happened. I decided I didn't want to know for sure, and in a perverse way began doing more physical exercise than I had in years. In the back of my mind I was daring my body to miscarry. In a way I was saying to myself, if I'm going to lose this pregnancy, I want to lose it now, before I invest in it, because I don't think I can stand losing it later.

One weekend we visited friends in West Chester, Pennsylvania. Bill and Anne live near Bill's father, who owns race horses and keeps retired ones in a pasture next to Bill's house. I accepted the invitation to ride, and found myself on a small saddle, on the huge back of a not-so-tired race horse. As we took off across the field I remember thinking if I was pregnant, it was going to have to be a healthy one to make it through this ride.

The next weekend we left the city again and visited friends who had access to a tennis court and swimming pool. Hugh and I played our typical game, which consists of his standing in one place while I run all over the court. Sweating and running, turning and lunging for the ball, again I thought, "Okay body, if you're going to miscarry, do it now."

At the end of September, certain I was pregnant, I finally went to Dr. Balick's office to take a pregnancy test.

"I'm sorry," said Maria, one of the nurses who had followed my two-year drama. "It's coming out negative." My heart fell six inches and lay motionless. I had no idea how badly I wanted to be pregnant until she told me I wasn't. In the back of my mind I had been so sure, but had imagined the whole thing. What did they call it, a pseudopregnancy? I didn't say anything, but kept looking at the test tube in disbelief.

"Okay, okay," Maria said. "I'll try it again. It's a new test, and I might have done something wrong." She reapplied the chemicals and checked her watch.

"Wait a minute. It's coming out positive. You are pregnant. Congratulations!"

My heart flew up to my throat, fell back again, and once more lay motionless. Now what was I going to do?

In several minutes all my bravado and positive thinking about being pregnant left me. I walked outside to 57th Street like a zombie, scarcely noticing the people and traffic. Images thundered through my mind with such force I finally paused and leaned against a stone wall. What if I lost this pregnancy too? Everything in me suddenly wished I wasn't pregnant and didn't have to live through eight more months of uncertainty.

"Oh God," I whispered. "Help me trust this one will work out. I don't want to spend a whole pregnancy in fear."

I noticed people staring at me, idly wondering if I were on drugs, or sick, or trying to scope out someone's apartment. "I'm pregnant!" I wanted to shout. "Don't you people understand what this means? I'm doing this thing again but I don't know if it's going to work!"

The drive of motherhood must be far deeper than rational thinking, because rationally I would never put myself through another pregnancy after losing two. Fall arrived in New York City, and I was pregnant for the third year in a row. Eight more months of waiting stretched before me like a prison sentence, and the only guarantee of success I had on the medical front was that someone I hardly knew told me he had removed tissue from my uterus while I was under anesthesia. It seemed a slim guarantee.

By this pregnancy, I bore no resemblance whatsoever to a glowing mother-to-be. It made me mad to see advertisements of radiant women in rocking chairs, caressing their curving bellies, staring dreamily at new baby furniture. I looked at upscale maternity stores selling leather skirts with expandable waists or pleated party dresses, and turned away thinking how stupid all the hype is when all I wanted was a baby.

Medically, Dr. Balick knew I needed the circlage again. He had seen my cervix starting to open at nine weeks, and wanted to do the procedure before there wasn't any cervix left to stitch.

I entered the hospital one more time. As I waited for the familiar trip to the operating room I prayed that if I were going to lose this pregnancy, that it happen immediately. I didn't want to go through another premature labor and emergency removal of the stitches.

This time I asked for sedation instead of general anesthesia, because I preferred being awake during the procedure, to being asleep but sick for three days from the drugs. Dr. Balick agreed, so I was awake but pleasantly removed during the entire thing. Recovery was simple, and I was home in a day with instructions to take it easy for a while and then proceed with caution.

A week later I went to see Dr. Balick for what would become my weekly visit. Sitting on the examination table, I saw the file folder that held my charts. It was now about two inches thick with papers sticking out in all directions. In it was the record of two full years of tries and misses, of procedures, and operations, of hopes rising and falling, of blood tests and urine tests and all the "scope" tests, and X-rays, and sonograms, and theories, and terminations.

It was extremely important to me that things be different this time around. I trusted that all the speculation was coming to an end, and that we had finally found my problem and fixed it. This time would be different because my uterus was different.

"I'm so glad I'm starting this pregnancy differently," I said to Dr. B.

"What do you mean?" he asked.

"Well, you know, the hysteroscopy and my uterus being fixed."

"Wait a minute," he said with his eyebrows up. "We can't guarantee that operation is going to make a difference."

"What are you talking about?" I said, my stomach starting to twist.

"We're hoping the septum had something to do with your previous losses, but we may never know for sure."

I stared at him dumbfounded. I had been sure we found my problem, and now I was hearing it was possible nothing was really different. It suddenly struck me full force that the medical world would offer no absolutes. In one minute I hated the entire medical profession for being willing to operate and then quick to backpedal when it came to a guarantee. I hated learning how little a doctor really knows, and I hated myself for so wholeheartedly relying on an operation to fix my problem.

It was the first time I looked at Dr. B and couldn't speak. My throat was tight and I thought I might cry, or throw up, or roll off the table and lie on the floor. How could they take away the thing I was relying on to make this pregnancy different? If they weren't sure, then what was I doing pregnant, and sewn up?

Was I supposed to live through the next twenty-nine weeks hoping maybe something might have changed in my body so it wouldn't spring into labor while I was at the office, or on the subway, or caught in a traffic jam?

I don't remember saying good-bye to Dr. B. I simply ended up on the street trying to digest the loss of my confidence.

A strange aspect of pregnancy is the realization there's no gracious way out of it. Once you've conceived, that baby will come out of you one way or another, dead or alive, prematurely, on time, or maybe two weeks late. Add to that the unrelenting reminders in your body day and night for three quarters of a year, and you end up with an altogether formidable experience, especially if there's reason to suspect something will go wrong.

I tried to be lighthearted. I tried being carefree about it. I tried to distract myself with my friendships, work, and other activities, but the fact remained I had a tremendously difficult time not wondering what would go wrong with this pregnancy, and when. I knew that every day I stayed pregnant was a victory, but every day also demanded more investment on my part both physically and emotionally, and made the prospect of losing it that much harder to bear.

For whatever reason, I couldn't maintain a clear picture of this pregnancy and believe without reservation that it would work. Over and over again someone would say to me, "Well, this one is it, isn't it? You're all fixed up now, and you'll have a healthy baby."

It was hard for me to agree. I didn't know if I was all fixed up, and I was afraid to commit myself to the idea and face one more disappointment. I still believed that one day I'd have a baby, but I didn't know if this was

the time. I couldn't see my way clear through the next
seven months to a happy ending.

Part of my daily routine at this time was walking to
work. It took almost an hour door-to-door, and I had
the pleasure of walking through Central Park for most
of it. The morning walk became my quiet time to think
and set my mind before the business of the day began.
Daily, I congratulated Frederick Law Olmstead on his
design of the park and persistence in making it happen
so that city dwellers for years to come could smell the
earth, recognize the seasons, and walk without company. At this time of day many solo walkers passed
through the park, respecting each other's need for nature.

Each morning I entered from the west side at about
66th Street, taking a footpath that dipped down, went
under a bridge, and eventually joined the main traffic
pattern of the park. Close to the entrance were benches,
almost always occupied by sleeping homeless men wrapped
in cardboard or old blankets. Sometimes a small fire
smoldered in a trash can, but I rarely saw any activity.

One morning, however, as I came down the path
they were all rising, and looking in my direction. I
considered walking on, trusting they were harmless as
well as homeless. A closer look at their faces and I
decided it was wiser not to find out. I veered off the
path into the underbrush.

I knew where I wanted to end up, and knew in which
direction the road lay, but couldn't see how to get
there. Instead of following a path, I had to climb over

some rocks and make my way through the bushes to get back on my usual route.

I climbed a small incline and pushed my way through a tangle of leaves and twigs, hoping to see the road. Instead I found more rocks to climb, and more bushes at the top. I felt a little silly in my dress and stockings scaling the rocks of Central Park, but having gone this far, I wasn't about to turn back.

Still heading in the direction I thought was right, I once more found my view obscured by tall bushes and trees. For a minute I wondered if I were lost, and thought how fitting it would be to have lived successfully in the wilds of Montana only to be lost forever in the bushes of Central Park. With a grunt, I stepped onto a big rock, and on the other side saw an uneven dirt path winding off through the trees.

It wasn't one of Mr. Olmstead's formal routes, but it was a path nevertheless, and I gratefully walked along it knowing I wasn't the first person to conquer this section of the park. Within minutes I recognized where I was, and joined up with the main road almost exactly at the point I anticipated.

I'm not one to seek meaning in trivial events, but my morning walk struck me with possibility. Just because there's not an obvious way to get to my goal, doesn't mean I won't get there. A totally unexpected route might open up and take me where I want to go.

I was the one who believed in believing, and in trusting God in spite of negative circumstances. More than once I had encouraged people not to get defeated in their minds. I needed to practice my own beliefs or dissolve in my own pool of worry.

I remembered years earlier how we got off the mountain the night our truck had the flat on MacDonald Pass. Crouching next to the snowdrift, we eventually noticed light coming over the peak of the mountain from the direction we had driven. While we waited for whatever it was to come into view, we tried to picture something large enough to pick up four extra passengers.

What eventually topped the crest of the pass was an enormous bus sending up swirls of snow in its wake. We flagged down the wary driver who agreed to take us on when he saw the stalled truck. We sat back in the reclining seats and enjoyed the warm ride to Missoula where we all, including the bus driver, went for steak and eggs at the Oxford Diner at 2 A.M. I later wrote in my diary: "When things seem bleak, hang in there. There could be a bus coming over the mountain."

I didn't need to deal with the remaining seven months of my pregnancy all at once. One day at a time was enough. Even if the medical prognosis was uncertain, and I couldn't see how my body would carry to term, it didn't mean there wasn't a way. Who knew what path might open up that wasn't visible yet, and who knew if there wasn't a bus coming over the mountain to help.

10 . Time Bomb

From the moment I learned I was pregnant for sure, there was not one day that didn't come down to a clear battle of faith versus fear. Depending on how I handled my mind, either faith or fear prevailed, and I reaped the resulting peacefulness or anxiety. I calculated at one point that in three years I had been pregnant for fourteen months and still didn't have a baby. Sometimes I felt my whole life could be summed up by the word *pregnant*, and I yearned to be dealing with another subject.

To this day I come across photographs of me taken during the third pregnancy, and my expression is always the same. It doesn't matter if the photo was taken inside or outside, in a crowd, alone, during a fancy occasion, or just in our living room, my face looks the same: grim. Just seeing the photographs reminds me of the battle that waged in my mind, and how hard I fought to hold on to positive thoughts when there was no evidence in the world to help me.

Because my previous losses occurred with no warning, I knew it was possible to miscarry at any moment.

Because the medical world was not certain what caused my losses, I couldn't rely on them for encouragement. Because no one really knew if the operation had fixed my problem, I couldn't rely on the fact that this pregnancy would be different from the others. No matter where I was, I felt like a time bomb, ticking away the minutes until some unknown signal set me off.

The mind has so many capacities we're not aware of until we test them. During this time, part of my mind became a calculator, always running, always computing the exact day of my pregnancy and how much time was left. NASA could not have monitored my pregnancy with more precision.

The average pregnancy takes forty weeks. I lost one pregnancy at twenty-four weeks, and another at twenty-one weeks. To a great extent I desperately wanted to make it to twenty-five weeks, just to break my own record. From there, twenty-eight weeks was the earliest I could give birth with the baby having a good chance of making it. Thirty-two weeks was considered safe as far as a baby that could make it and lead a normal life. Each week after that brought more and more opportunity for a healthy, happy baby.

By this time in my childbearing career I knew exactly what day I had conceived, my due date, and the significance of every one of the 278 days in between. Virtually without my realizing it, my mind could compute at any moment precisely where I was in the pregnancy. Sometimes I blocked it out, promising myself not to calculate the days until the end of each week. But, inside I registered the passing of each day, and knew what it meant.

On a larger scale, I knew Thanksgiving was my three-month mark, Christmas was four months, and January 23rd would mark my twenty-fifth, record-breaking week. To my thinking, if I made it to the twenty-fifth week, it indicated something truly different about this pregnancy. Most days I wished I could fold up the calendar and step immediately into January 23d, skipping the months in between.

I wasn't proud of this detailed computation of each day. I was impressed, however, at what my mind could do under pressure, and wished I had trained it better before the pressure started.

To many people in my office, apartment building, and neighborhood, I'm sure I appeared my normal self. I had been pregnant, or recovering from it, so many times that some people had never known me not tight-lipped, wearing baggy shirts, flat-heeled shoes, and rubbing my stomach.

Recently a friend said to me, "You sure were calm during that pregnancy, in your heart you must have believed everything would be all right." Her comment took me aback because all I can remember was the underlying struggle to control my mind that took place during every phone call, business appointment, lunch date, meeting, and free moment I had.

Every afternoon did bring me some relief because of a game I played in my brain. Both of my previous losses began when my water broke, followed by heavy con-

tractions. Both losses had started by lunchtime. Therefore, every day when I made it past lunch and was still
pregnant, I counted that day a victory. Many evenings I
went home from work, put my feet up on the couch and
didn't move again until bedtime. I rode out the end of
the day shoring up energy for the next morning.

Another game I played was what would I do if my
water broke and I did go into labor. If I did go into
labor, the circlage needed to be cut before it ripped out.
If my water broke as it had the previous times, I needed
to get to the hospital quickly where Dr. Balick could
clip the stitches and deliver the baby. Each of the
previous times had given me about four hours between
the water breaking and delivery. In my thinking I never
wanted to be more than four hours from a hospital or
medical help.

In the city, I made a mental habit of noting where
the nearest phone was, and planning my escape route
should I ever need it. I had already lived through
my water breaking in public, so I was no longer as
concerned about the embarrassment as much as the
logistics of getting through the city streets to Roosevelt
Hospital.

Again during this pregnancy Dr. Balick seemed to
think bed rest wasn't necessary. He felt that lying down
for the pregnancy wouldn't help me but, rather, would
give me too much time to think. He did, however,
caution me to avoid stairs as much as possible, not to
strain in any way, and certainly not to run or move too
quickly.

In October my parents made an offer that forced me to break out of my self-imposed prison. They were going to live in London for a month, and would bring Hugh and me over for a few days if we wanted. It sounded too good to pass up so we planned four days overseas when I would be in my fourth month of the pregnancy.

I went anticipating a good time, but not before I mentally prepared myself for any eventuality. I knew the flight time was approximately six or seven hours, so as long as I didn't go into labor at the beginning of the flight, I would have enough time to land and get to a doctor. In London my parents had good friends, one of whom was an Ob/Gyn, so we planned on my seeing her if I had any trouble during the four days.

Upon arrival in London, we negotiated so many flights of stairs at the airport, train stations, buses, and buildings that I made up for three previous months of caution in one day. In addition to having to carry luggage, I was exhausted from traveling and lack of sleep. I finally lay down on the bed where my parents were staying, and waited for labor to start. When nothing happened, I got back up and thought about shopping.

During the evening my parents entertained guests, one of whom was the British Ob/Gyn and friend of the family. My father passed drinks around, and I took my customary soda instead of alcohol. I looked up and saw the doctor smiling at me.

"You Americans," she said, laughing. "You're all so health conscious. Probably the best thing for you right now would be a good drink."

"But," I protested, "we've been told so much about how alcohol and caffeine can hurt the pregnancy."

"Maybe a bottle of Scotch every day," she answered. "But not one drink. As a matter of fact, if your uterus began to contract, a good drink could help relax it."

Of all the medical advice I'd heard, this was one idea I instantly claimed for my own. I exchanged my soda for a glass of wine and did likewise many more times before the pregnancy was over.

Back in the United States at holiday time I faced Christmas, which was also my twenty-first week of pregnancy, the point at which I lost the previous baby. I wanted to tiptoe through the week, barely speaking, barely breathing, just waiting to see what happened.

December 25th approached, and Hugh and I planned to stay in our apartment and not celebrate. We weren't going to buy each other presents, or go to a lot of parties, or get into the shopping frenzy of the city. This was going to be a stress-free Christmas.

We soon discovered how difficult it is not to observe a holiday that the entire world seems to embrace. In mid-December we began getting phone calls from friends who were coming to the city to see the lights and shop. Then we got gifts in the mail from our families, and cards from faraway places, and someone brought a small Norfolk Pine into the living room, and by Christmas Eve we were planning a roast beef dinner for eight.

On December 25th, I broke down and decorated the Norfolk Pine with cranberries and plaid ribbon, and Hugh and I exchanged gifts we promised we wouldn't buy each other. Ten of us who had all thought we'd spend the day alone, ended up eating together, and when all was said and done, we had guests for fourteen days during that holiday season.

With all the guests, cooking, conversations, and activity in the apartment, my twenty-first week passed without notice. I was thankful I hadn't sat at home alone, holding my breath, and waiting for the worst. But somehow I still had to make it through eleven more weeks before the real danger was over.

The New Year began in a slump. Many people were still on vacation, and work was slow. January looked endless. New York dumped its Christmas frosting within a week, and went back to its true nature. New snow turned to black slush on the sidewalks, and curbs were lined with abandoned Christmas trees and tinsel waiting to be eaten by the sanitation trucks.

At the office I forced myself to do small, ongoing projects for the architects. Even while working with Peggy, if I continued to work periodically for the architects I stayed on their insurance plan. "Face it," I said to myself one morning. "The only reason you're working on these projects is to keep the health insurance."

I recognized my own dishonesty, but didn't know how to change the situation. The work for the architects meant traveling all over New York City in the cold and slush, doing interviews, looking at design projects, and talking with clients. It strained my pregnancy, but it also made a world of difference in the medical bills we had to pay. I didn't like doing a job for the wrong reasons, and vowed one day to work exactly as I wanted, not just for an insurance plan.

Meanwhile, I was in a difficult time of the pregnancy, and still zooming around New York City looking at office designs. "When is this going to end?" I asked myself, reluctantly following a client up two flights of stairs to see some marvelous installation. "I'm tired of this never-ending caution, wondering if I'm triggering labor with my every step. It's like a weight around my neck wherever I go."

We found ourselves on the wrong floor, and had to go back down two flights, and up again through a different stairwell. "I want another concern in my life besides pregnancy," I continued to myself. "I want to run down the street, jump on a bicycle, drive to the mountains and go skiing. I want to climb stairs without hesitation and drag heavy boxes around the apartment. I want to wear normal clothes, laugh with friends, and sit through a movie without wondering if I'm going to be forced to make a quick exit. I want to wake up and have the uncertainty be gone." But the January days were unrelenting.

True to her predictions, Meggan had become pregnant the first time she tried, and was a full eight weeks ahead of me in her textbook pregnancy. We shared many of our thoughts on the prospect of motherhood, but never without wondering whether I would indeed make it to motherhood in the first place.

Jodie, however, became an accomplice of a different sort. She too was pregnant, six weeks ahead of me, and was also one of Dr. Balick's patients. She too had the circlage, and wondered on a daily basis if her pregnancy would succeed. We communicated on the same level of agitation, both being high-risk patients, and both counting the days and sometimes hours of our pregnancies.

We don't share much else in common, but the bond of our pregnancies brought us very close together for that period of time. We handled the same pressures in our two distinctly different manners. Always the artist, Jodie's appearance grew more flamboyant over the months as mine grew more somber. As her belly grew, she adopted wispy leopard scarves, mens' Hawaiian shirts, and printed high-top sneakers. Working at home, she whipped up little gifts for Dr. Balick and his staff on major holidays, or for no reason at all.

Every week, Jodie and I had back-to-back appointments with Dr. Balick. The appointments ran like a lifeline through the dark winter months, and gave me a point of contact each week to review the pregnancy and record the progress. Jodie and I looked forward to our half hour with the doctor when we could say, "Look, we made it another week!" and solemnly pencil in the following week's visit.

As the months went on, we made a minor event out of each visit. At the time, Dr. Balick worked in an old wing of Roosevelt Hospital that was long overdue for renovation. The doctors, nurses, and receptionists were all over each other in a central open space, answering each other's phones, yelling comments back and forth, and minding each other's business. Nothing was sacred, and Jodie and I gratefully joined the merriment each week.

Dr. Balick was in his prime in this atmosphere, where we could hear peels of laughter coming from whatever examining room he was in. One time he told me he would never win any awards for academic excellence, or make it far in hospital politics, but he was the right doctor if a patient was depressed. I carefully weighed whether I needed a renowned doctor in a quiet, carpeted office with abstract prints on the walls, or this funny, caring man who worked in friendly chaos. I needed funny and caring.

Each visit became a milestone for Jodie and me, and we left the office together to have a cup of tea and a talk before going home. In spite of our different styles we found we had adopted similar habits in our pregnancies. We both confessed to checking our underpants for blood every time we went to the bathroom, and to going so far as buying only white toilet paper so any hint of blood could be detected.

We both could describe in detail each pain, twinge, and cramp of every day, when it happened, and what it might mean. We both read books in bed, lying on our left side because we heard it was better for the uterus. We both went to sleep when the pressure grew too great, and awoke in the middle of the night wondering if we were in labor.

In other ways, we were totally different. Jodie's method was to talk about pregnancy all the time with everyone. Mine was to dodge the subject. Jodie read every newsletter, baby report, and magazine she could. I avoided them. Jodie bought little clothes, put baby furniture on layaway, and tortured herself by watching mothers and babies in the park. With dedication, I ignored mothers and babies, blocked out any thought of little clothes, strollers, or diaper bags, and purposely didn't ask Hugh where our baby furniture was stored.

When the time came, Jodie decided to have the amniocentesis test, and I did not. I had spent so many months trying to keep a baby inside me, that I knew I wouldn't be able to choose an abortion even if the baby were determined to be unhealthy.

Both Jodie and I found ourselves calling Dr. Balick at the slightest cause for alarm. The phone company mistakenly listed his home number in the New York phone book, and neither of us hesitated one second in calling if we thought the situation was serious. His patience was admirable.

One night in my fourth month I began to cramp and thought the pregnancy was probably ending. I called Dr. Balick's home.

"What am I going to do?" I said to him in a weary voice. "I can't handle losing this pregnancy, and I'm starting to cramp."

"There's nothing you can do right now," he said patiently, having been awakened from sleep. "If you're going to miscarry, it's going to happen. We can only make it less painful. Unfortunately, you have to wait it out."

"But what can I do?" I kept pushing.

"Alison," he said slowly. "The only viable alternative for you right now," and he paused again, "is suicide."

With the phone propped on one shoulder, I began to laugh. He was right. I could either wait it out or kill myself. If I kept going, I might have a baby.

"Thank you." I chuckled. "Good night."

"Good night."

The next day my cramps were gone, and I found that Jodie also had been on the phone with Dr. B the night before. Between us, we aged the man beyond his years.

My life turned into a series of small goals, and I dragged myself from one to the next with dogged determination. In December I made something I had thought about for a long time, to mark my progress. I took a large piece of artist's drawing paper, bought colored markers, found a ruler in the house, and constructed a pregnancy goal calendar.

The calendar formed a large grid with sixteen boxes. Each box represented one week of the pregnancy from twenty-five through forty. In each box I wrote the pregnancy week, the actual date, and a comment, and then hung the paper on the side of my bureau where I could see it each morning. At the end of every week I X-ed through the box with a red marker.

Week twenty-five said "record breaking," and on January 23d, I took my red marker and slowly crossed off the box. I had finally made it farther than ever before.

On February 6th, I drew another X through the box that said "Week twenty-seven" and a quote from Jeremiah:

"Behold, I am the God of all flesh, is there anything too hard for me?"

Week twenty-eight ended on February 13th, and as I made my X, I entered the time period when premature delivery meant the baby had a good chance. I looked across the calendar to week thirty-two where I had written "Champagne Toast," and knew the pressure wouldn't really let up for another four weeks.

I still went to work every day, but had given up my daily walk. March brought nasty ice and cold, and one day I missed my footing on Broadway and fell on the sidewalk, after which I started taking the bus to work. Even though it meant instant contact with fifty people, I looked pregnant enough that someone usually offered me a seat.

The number 104 bus runs directly past my building, but I boarded it a little to the north, and then rode back down Broadway past my own apartment. From the bus, I could see one of the storefronts directly under our apartment that had been boarded up for months waiting for a new tenant. Rumor told us it would be a fast-food hamburger place, which meant cockroaches and grease for those of us living above.

In my fight against fear, I had developed a mental exercise on the bus to block out the grumbling passengers and newspaper headlines, and settle my mind for the day. Each morning I closed my eyes and mentally took all my worries about the pregnancy and lumped them into one box. Then I pictured myself standing on the box and looking up unobstructed to a sky filled with stars. "All my problems are under my feet," I'd point out to myself, "but up there anything is possible. Keep your thoughts up there, not down here."

One day I added as an afterthought, "I sure wouldn't mind some encouragement down here." When I opened my eyes I was staring at my own building and several construction workers who were at that moment unveiling the new storefront sign. I looked with resignation but, instead of golden arches, I saw chrome lettering I didn't recognize.

The bus jerked forward and I had to stand up to read the sign as we moved away. Big silver letters spelled out the word *Mothercare* with another small sign underneath.

"Am I hallucinating?" I asked the unsuspecting woman next to me. "Does that sign say McDonald's or Mothercare?"

"Mothercare," she said helpfully, "and underneath it says: 'All your needs for the newborn.' "

"Thank you," I replied. "That's all I wanted to know."

After work I cautiously looked again at the new storefront, which indeed advertised a store for the new mother and baby, scheduled to open before my due date, barely fifteen feet beneath my apartment window.

It was March 6th, and I crossed out week thirty-one on my calendar with its comment: "Hold your breath." In one more week I would open a bottle of champagne and stretch my face into a genuine smile.

It was also March when I was invited to two baby showers for the two women in my life who were pregnant. Both Meggan and Jodie were nearing their due dates, leaving me eight and six weeks behind, respectively. Meggan was due at the end of March, and Jodie at the beginning of April. I was due on May 8th, which sounded to me as far away as the next century.

The gap between my pregnancy and Jodie's, which had been negligible all winter, now seemed insurmountable. While she coasted into her thirty-eighth week and had her circlage removed, I crawled into my thirty-second week, just over the line for a healthy baby, with complications of course.

I attended Jodie's shower and organized Meggan's, all the while in a mental fog. Sitting in their homes, looking at their presents and their plans to house a newborn, I was completely lost. It dawned on me that as I had so thoroughly avoided any investment in my pregnancy, I was also thoroughly unprepared for the reality of having a baby. I had been pregnant for so long with no baby that I wasn't sure one would come along this time either.

When it had been time for me to enroll in a childbirth class, I misplaced the phone number, missed the deadline, and didn't call to see if there was still room. I didn't care about the birth experience or whether I had drugs or not, how long I was in labor, or whether it was a boy or a girl. My concern was simply to give birth to a living baby. I literally never considered what happened after the baby was born. My imagination never strayed that far.

Suddenly the prospects overwhelmed me. Hugh had hidden the baby furniture we owned, and I didn't know

where it was, what it was, or where to put it if I wanted
it. I hadn't thought about names, baby clothes, little
toys, or diapers. I had so carefully avoided planning for
a baby that my mind drew an automatic blank whenever the subject came up. Looking at Jodie's array of
preparations made me want to cry. I would never understand it all, and didn't know where to begin.

Everything new mothers drooled over, I had avoided,
and now I faced the entire display in Jodie's living
room. There were bumper sets for a crib (I couldn't
remember if we had a crib), undershirts (what did a
baby wear?), rattles (where did one buy toys for a
newborn?), strollers—one lightweight, one deluxe (where
does one buy a stroller in New York City?), blankets
(couldn't we use one of ours?), a walker, car seat, diaper
pail, mobiles, music boxes, piles of receiving blankets
(what's that?), kimono shirts (oriental clothes?), and a
plastic tub for giving the baby a bath.

For several moments I became fixated on the baby
bath. It symbolized for me, not only my lack of knowl-
edge, but my lack of resources in caring for a baby.
How, when, and where does a baby take a bath? I had
no idea. Not only that, I didn't know where to learn
and I certainly didn't know where to buy a baby bath of
my own.

I was now faced with a double dilemma. It was still
quite early to deliver, but even if I did deliver a real
baby, I had no idea how to care for it. New York City
isn't known for being a friendly town, and I knew no
neighbors with babies. My mother lived 200 miles away

and couldn't remember if she ever bought a baby bath or exactly how many times you use it if you have one. I had so determinedly dragged myself from one day to the next that I never looked ahead to the end result, and now I was completely unprepared.

On March 19th, Meggan called me from her home. "I think I'm in labor," she said calmly. "Konrad's out in Brooklyn, so I'm going to take a bath and then call the midwives." An hour later, she called back. "We're going to the hospital. The contractions are getting a little strong."

"Does it hurt?" I asked, not knowing what else to say.

"It's a little rough. I better be going. We'll call when it's over."

I hung up and stared at my desk. One down, two to go. I was approaching my thirty-third week, Jodie her thirty-ninth, and Meggan was going to the hospital. Things were really happening.

I left work that day and detoured far to the West side. I ended up outside Roosevelt Hospital, where Meggan was in some stage of labor or delivery. On impulse I went inside and made it to the maternity floor without being stopped. My face was familiar enough to the staff that they let me pass without question, and I went through the swinging doors and around the corner to the birthing room.

There I stopped. Meggan was inside that room and I was there without permission and didn't know what to do next. On a white board by the nurses' station I could see Meggan's name and numbers scrawled next to it. Apparently she was 8 cm. dilated, and either delivering right now or very close to it.

I turned back to the birthing room, and suddenly a gasp came from the other side of the door, followed by low voices and a louder gasp. I stood in the hallway staring at the door, listening to my friend give birth. "I'm here Meggan," I whispered. "This is it, isn't it? I bet you're doing great. Hey, let me know, okay . . . ?" I slowly turned, retraced my steps, and went out into the cold, early evening.

On March 27th, I crossed out week thirty-four on my calendar. Meggan had a baby girl. I visited her and heard the stories of the first strange days with a strange baby in the house. I calculated my own dates for the thousandth time and saw there were still six weeks to go, with a full two weeks before Dr. Balick would clip my circlage and let my body take its natural course.

That evening Hugh was working late. Everything had started to change lately, throwing me even more off-balance. My nonchalant husband had started working as a stagehand at different television studios, taking on more and more hours. "He's turning into a father," one friend told me. "Responsibility is starting to hit."

People at my own job were beginning to look at me with strange expressions. "You'll be leaving us soon," they seemed to say. Even Peggy took it for granted I was going to give birth soon, and stopped scheduling me into upcoming projects.

All of this made me very nervous. Apparently these people thought I'd really have a baby. Daily I went to the office, not knowing what else to do. If I stayed home I was only reminded of how unprepared I was for this baby business. It was easier to go to work and wait as I had done for three years.

I reflected on all this as I stood in my kitchen, waiting for Hugh to come home. Why did I think having this baby would never happen? The apartment buzzer interrupted my thoughts and I could hear the voice of one of our friends through the intercom. Dennis worked in television and was the one who introduced Hugh to the different studios. He arrived at our apartment door with a bulky object under his arm wrapped in a garbage bag. I waited to see what would appear from this curious cover.

"I was on the set this week," Dennis explained, talking about one of the daytime soap operas. "And one of the girls on the show was having a baby. I don't know how it happened, but we ended up with three of the same prop. They asked if anyone wanted this, and I thought of you."

With that he pulled back the bag to reveal a white baby bath with a sponge liner and little shelf, with the label still on it.

I started to laugh. "What's the matter," Dennis asked. "You don't need it?"

"No," I answered. "It's exactly what I need—something to help me believe I'm going to have this baby."

He refrained comment, apparently thinking pregnant women don't have to make any sense. After he left, I sat on a chair with my feet propped up, looking at the baby bath, and wondering. I sat that way for a long time, until Hugh came home and gently propelled me down the hall to bed.

11 . Delivery

All my hours, days, weeks, and months of waiting were coming to an end. The future was now the present, and I didn't know how to handle it. Jodie and I went to see Dr. Balick together, she filled to capacity with baby, and I pleasantly round but not very big.

"Have you two thought," said Dr. B with uncustomary seriousness, "that you are going to have babies? All you've talked about is this pregnancy, but do you have any idea what it's like to have a baby in the house? You think pregnancy takes a long time! You're entering a lifetime commitment with this event. Has that sunk in yet?"

I thought for a minute but had no idea what he was talking about. As far as I could see my life was a series of pregnancies. A baby was a different matter entirely.

Jodie and I left together, chatting about her preparations for delivery. She had spent the week perfecting her state of readiness. Her hospital bag contained pocket-size shampoo, soap, toothpaste, and skin lotion, as well as nightgown, hair dryer, underwear, slippers, and nursing bra. Another bag for the baby had diapers, little clothes, receiving blankets, and booties. She had prepared meals in advance for her husband, had readied both a crib and a cradle for the new baby, and had a friend paint her toenails, which she could no longer reach.

All I had was a baby bath.

I didn't hear from Jodie for two days. When she finally called, she was a mother. Her voice went from thrill, to awe, to giggling. It was wonderful, it was indescribable, it was new life.

I hung up and looked down at my own stomach. It didn't seem very big, and I had never felt kicking as other people described it. Maybe there wasn't a baby in there after all, but I had made the whole thing up.

"God, this is sick thinking," I said out loud. "I'm so used to disappointment, I can't believe it's actually going to happen. What am I going to do for the next five weeks, visit other peoples' babies?" The next day I had my answer.

I went to work as usual and spent the day putting together a proposal to promote a television travel program. Peggy and I enjoyed the brainstorming part of the project and allowed ourselves to dream up outlandish ideas, which we then pared down to reality.

It was Friday, April 3rd, and I could mark off on my calendar exactly thirty-five weeks of pregnancy. Five weeks to go. I took a bus home as usual and decided I would have to find one of my books on pregnancy exercises to relieve an ache in my lower back. At home,

I changed into pants and got down on the living room floor, holding the book above my head. It was the first time I tried a pregnancy exercise, not having wanted to invest early if the pregnancy wasn't going to make it. I tried to lift my leg like the picture in the book, and dutifully repeated the motion several times.

Hugh came home late that night, and we finally sat down to eat a sandwich at about 9 P.M. Five bites into the ham and cheese, and I was overwhelmed with embarrassment.

"Hugh," I said cautiously. "I think I just wet my pants in a big way."

I pushed back my chair and headed for the bathroom where another gush of water fell out of me. "Oh God, this is it, isn't it? I'm not peeing; my water just broke!"

"Hugh," I yelled. "I'm in labor. It's happening. Call Dr. Balick. We don't have much time."

Still struggling with my pants, I grabbed the phone myself and dialed Dr. B's answering service.

"I thought you wanted me to call him," Hugh was standing in the hallway smiling.

"How can you be so calm?" I hissed, then told the woman on the phone to page Dr. Balick and get him to the hospital immediately. Not convinced she understood me, I quickly dialed Dr. Balick's home phone, got no answer, and called the answering service again.

"Calm down," Hugh said, taking the phone. "We've got time. The baby's going to be fine. You're thirty-five weeks pregnant. Babies live when they're born at thirty-five weeks."

I, however, was inconsolable. The only thing I could think about was how quickly everything progressed after my water broke, how much I wanted to see Dr. Balick's face, and how badly I wanted the stitches cut before they ripped out.

The answering service must have reached Dr. B, because Hugh hung up the phone, got our coats, and opened the door. Typically, we left for the hospital with the clothes on our back and cab money; no small suitcase, no shampoo, no nightgown, and no baby blanket.

Hugh hailed a cab in seconds, and we raced down West End Avenue toward 59th Street and Roosevelt Hospital. At 61st Street another gush of water came out of me, resoaking my pants.

We tumbled onto the sidewalk outside Roosevelt, and I realized another couple was already climbing into the cab, thinking how lucky they were to find a taxi so easily. They took off and I stood on the sidewalk thinking, "Boy are you going to be surprised by that back seat."

"Coming?" said Hugh, holding the door of the hospital open, and I followed him in before the cab driver was able to back up the street and attack me.

We walked down the halls to the maternity ward, soaked pants clinging to my legs, and cramps gripping my stomach. Several nurses took one look at me and herded us into a room, undressed me, and put me in a gown. Before I knew it, I was hooked up to a fetal monitor. Where was Dr. Balick?

About 10 P.M., Dr. Balick skidded into the room. He had been at a New Jersey airport, ready to take off, when the answering service reached him. "If you didn't make it here tonight, I would have killed you," I said simply.

He didn't answer, but was busy piecing together the situation. In fifty minutes I had gone from no contractions to contractions three minutes apart. He ordered the right equipment to cut my circlage, and I was wheeled into another room.

I couldn't wait to get the stitches out of me. For some reason I was most concerned that they not rip out before Dr. Balick could cut them. A nurse handed Dr. Balick some scissors, which turned out to be the wrong length. Calling for longer scissors, he became a different doctor than the one I had known. The humor was replaced by intense, concise orders to everyone present, including me. Maybe this was what he meant by being a bastard when necessary.

Meanwhile I couldn't catch my breath, but was shaking, and gasping, and trying to sit up, trying to breathe deeply, and listen to Hugh and the nurse and Dr. Balick all at the same time. It all moved so fast. Later Dr. Balick told me that when he finally clipped the stitches my cervix flew open about seven centimeters, and I was immediately ready to deliver.

It was his voice that finally rose above everything else in the room. "Everybody shut up. I'm giving the orders. Listen to me and do what I say."

"But, but but . . . ," I stammered.

"That means you," he said pointing at me. "Shut up and listen to me."

"But I'm scared," I said in one breath.

"You are not," he countered. "I know you, and you are not scared."

I considered this and thought maybe I wasn't after all.

"Now look at me and breathe when I say to."

I tried to concentrate on him and get on top of my body. His blue eyes disappeared for a moment, satisfied I was sufficiently under control.

"Humph," came his voice from somewhere at the end of the table. "I'm not going to deliver this baby."

"Wh-, wh-, why?" I was yelling again.

"It has more hair than I do. Now, push."

Three pushes later the baby was out. There was a moment's pause, and then Hugh, Dr. Balick, and the nurse all told me it was a girl. A pediatrician took her to the side to check her out. The nurse looked at me, waiting for my reaction.

"It is alive?" I asked. Having given birth before but with no life, I wanted to assure myself this time was different.

The nurse looked horrified. "What a terrible question," she said. "Of course it's alive. And it's not an it, it's a she."

The focus of the room shifted quickly from me to the new baby. For so long the emphasis had been on me—my blood pressure, cervix, urine, heartbeat, weight, and contractions. Now it was on the tiny infant in the corner—her blood sugar, urine, bowels, body temperature, lungs, eyes, and reflexes.

Dr. Balick was stitching me up, once more relaxed and joking. I understood. His work was over. I was his patient, not the new baby, and I was fine.

Within minutes I was in a softly lit room, wearing a fresh gown, once more staring at the ceiling and holding Hugh's hand. The baby was in a nursery somewhere for further observation because the pediatrician wanted to monitor her heartbeat. Hugh noticed a phone in the room, and we called our parents.

"Guess who came to dinner . . . ?" I told them: "Your granddaughter."

Then Dr. Balick came in to talk with us. The baby was fine, just small—an even five pounds. They were keeping her warm in a room down the hall. I felt oddly unconcerned. All I had wanted to do was deliver a healthy baby, and now it was over.

Exhilarated and tired at the same time, I listened to Hugh and Dr. Balick talking in low voices. It was almost midnight and the hospital had quieted down. Hugh was smiling, I was shaking a little even under several blankets, and Dr. B talked nonstop, unwinding from the event that had taken forty minutes of his time, and all of his concentration.

I drifted in and out of the conversation, my mind still trying to catch up to what happened. The last thing I was sure of was the ham and cheese sandwich almost three hours before.

I tried to focus on Dr. B's voice. "I just want you to know," he was saying, "that the birth of this child was about 10 percent the medical profession and 90 percent whatever it is you believed in that kept you going."

Hugh and I smiled. I'll bet you'll deny ever saying that, I thought, but I'm not going to forget it.

Hugh helped wheel me into my room for the night, and decided to go home for some sleep before coming back in the morning. I was alone with a roommate on the other side of a curtain, who had her one-day-old baby next to the bed. That made me wonder where my own baby was, and I rang for a nurse who was just coming on duty. She went to find out, and I lay back wondering if I really had a baby after all.

I could hear my roommate moaning in the other bed, and I called out in the dark, asking her what was wrong.

"My breasts," she said in a tone of dismay. "They're like rocks. I think my milk came in, but I decided not to breast feed. What do I do?"

"Suffer," I thought vengefully, then changed my mind and said aloud, "Don't worry, they'll go down eventually. Just don't press on them."

What a strange culmination to my months of waiting and wanting. I finally had a baby but didn't know where she was. I was in a dark room with a moaning woman, and the nurse had seemingly forgotten about me. Reality is just never like the pictures you make up in your mind. You couldn't possibly imagine all the elements that will actually make up the situation when it happens.

I shut my eyes and tried to relax every part of my body. "God, help me," I prayed. "Somewhere in this hospital is my baby, but I don't know where. I just know we did it, and you didn't bring me this far to let me down, so take care of her wherever she is."

I could feel sleep creeping into my thoughts. "And we need to name her sometime," I continued. "And, oh yes. Thank you. Thank you so much, I mean really, thank you."

The next thing I knew I was waking up and it was about 6 A.M. still with no sign of my baby. Painfully I stood up and shuffled my way out the door into the hallway, knowing someone would notice me and point me in the right direction. A new nurse came along, figured out who I was, and took me down the hall to the nursery where my little girl was in a special warmer.

I peered down at her face and tiny body curled up as if still in the womb, and felt the enormous collision of all my months of expectation with the reality of having a baby. She was funny looking because her nose went over to one side, and her eyes were puffy, and she was so absolutely tiny, weighing as much as a bag of sugar, which the nurse pointed out to me, and I was supposed to know what to do with her.

I had thought that once the baby was born, time would stand still and I could simply hold this new life. I couldn't have been more wrong. From the moment the nurse told me her body temperature was good, and transferred her to my arms, there was always a situation to handle: feeding, sterilizing, diapering, holding, cleaning. And one more question to answer: When will we leave the hospital, what will she wear, how can I walk when it hurts so much, what do I do about her jaundice?

At some point my mother arrived, and Hugh came back, and Peggy came in with my favorite Japanese food in a take-out box, and we all stared at this tiny baby who was as yellow as a banana with jaundice, and still had a crooked nose, but was, of course, beautiful.

The action never stopped or even slowed down. I tried to nurse her, but she would have none of it. A kindly nurse tried to make her take the nipple, but she only wanted the bottle of sugar water. And I tried and tried to get her to nurse, and finally picked her up at 2 A.M. when everything was quiet and we were alone, but she still wouldn't do it.

While I fumbled in bed in the dark, another nurse came by and told me the baby would starve if I didn't learn to breast feed. That made me cry and I called Hugh in the middle of the night, who told me to tell the nurse to go to hell and of course the kid would breast feed when she was good and ready to do it.

First thing in the morning, Hugh was back in the hospital room with an idea. He put some of the sugar water on my nipples, and held the baby up to let her taste it. Without a second thought, she took the nipple in her mouth and began to nurse, and Hugh looked at me as if to say, "So what was the big deal?"

Suddenly it was time to go home because this little girl, who had dropped to four pounds, ten ounces, gained weight and hit the five-pound mark again. It was two days since her arrival, and we were being cast out to let the next patient have a bed.

My Mom disappeared for an hour and came back with a big bag from the Mothercare store, filled with little clothes so the baby wouldn't go home naked. Hugh came in with pants and sneakers for me since I had thrown away the clothes I had worn to the hospital, and it was cold outside, so the nurse pulled a stocking cap over the baby's head and told me to keep it on her until the weather got warmer because she couldn't afford to lose heat.

I really didn't have a clue about what to do with the baby, and forgot what the nurse told me about bathing her. She seemed to cry a lot, and for heaven's sake we didn't even have a name for her yet or a place for her to sleep. Mom told me my brother fit in a bureau drawer, and I thought about that all the way down in the elevator and onto the street.

Hugh hailed a cab and we climbed in the back seat with me holding this tiny bundle of new life wrapped in oversized clothes. I looked down at the little yellow face sticking out from under the stocking cap, and thought it was the most vulnerable thing I'd ever seen in my whole life. Then she started to cry, and I began bouncing my knees up and down to calm her.

I looked out the window and saw a bum right next to the cab lean over and spit on the curb. He didn't even know or care that three feet away from him I was leaving the hospital as I had done so many times before, only this time, finally, I had a baby in my arms. Then the situation seemed so poignant I started to cry too, silent streams of warm, thankful tears, and outside it began to rain.

My heart felt fuller than it had ever been in my life, and I thought that, whatever we called this child, one of her names had to be Grace, because it just has to be grace that she was finally in my arms. And I would need a lot more grace from now on, because a desire of my heart had been fulfilled and I had to learn what to do with it.

Index

Circlage procedure
(*continued*)
  timing performance of,
  107
Contractions in labor,
  16–17, 26, 27
Crisis, reactions during,
  22, 25

D & C (Dilation and
  curettage), xii, xiii,
  xviii
Debra, 29–30, 64, 92
Dennis, 178
DES (Diethylstilbestrol),
  8–10, 57, 60, 134,
  135
  malformed uterus due to,
  101
  problems with, 8–10
Dilation and curettage. *See*
  D & C
Doctor's office, atmosphere
  in, 9

Elizabeth, Princess, 41, 42,
  44–45
Ended pregnancy. *See* Pregnancy loss

Father (of Alison), 76
  delivery of child by,
  43–44

First failed pregnancy, xv,
  1–12
  emotional reactions af-
  ter, 27–37
  labor in, 17, 21
  milk production follow-
  ing, 60–63, 65
  other peoples' reactions
  to, 66–68
  recovering from, 52–73
  return to work after,
  70–73
  search for cause of, 60–63
  shock following, 52–53,
  60, 65
  women with similar ex-
  periences, 68–69

Gilliatt, Sir William, 41–46
God, belief in, 7

"High-risk" pregnancies,
  32–33
Hugh, xvi, 3, 4, 11, 15–16,
  18, 21–24, 27–32,
  35, 37, 38, 49–51, 59,
  60, 62–64, 74–99,
  113, 114, 117, 118,
  120, 121, 124, 136,
  143, 146, 147,
  149–151, 164, 165,
  170, 174, 177–179,
  182–190
  on children, 98–99

About the Author

ALISON FREELAND received her BA from Brown University in 1976, and currently resides in New York City with her husband, Hugh, and daughter, Jessica.